Forgotten by Time

Forgotten by Time:

A Book of Living Fossils

BY ROBERT SILVERBERG

Illustrated by
Leonard Everett Fisher

Thomas Y. Crowell Company • New York

Manufactured in the United States of America
Library of Congress Catalog Card No. 66-11950
ISBN 0-690-31343-8
Published in Canada by Fitzhenry & Whiteside Limited, Toronto
3 4 5 6 7 8 9 10

Books by the Author

THE AUK, THE DODO, AND THE ORYX:
Vanished and Vanishing Creatures
SCIENTISTS AND SCOUNDRELS:
A Book of Hoaxes
FORGOTTEN BY TIME:
A Book of Living Fossils
GHOST TOWNS OF THE AMERICAN WEST

Contents

One: THE IDEA OF CHANGE

IN 1835, A BRITISH ARCHAEOLOGIST named George Finlay did some digging at a place called Pikermi, in Greece. He was looking for relics of Greek civilization. Instead he found some old bones—the remains of animals that had lived there many thousands of years ago.

Other scientists came to dig at Pikermi. They learned that many animals had been buried there. Long ago—and no one then could say *how* long ago—a river had dug a deep canyon near the town. Over the centuries a number of beasts had fallen into the canyon and had been buried by river mud. Their bones had been preserved. Scientists call such bones *fossils,* from the Latin word, *fossilis,* which means "dug up."

One of the fossils found at Pikermi looked something like a giraffe, but a very strange giraffe. Its body was giraffelike, but its legs were shorter than a giraffe's, and its neck was hardly longer than a horse's. Its discoverers named it *Helladotherium,* "the Greek mammal." They decided that it must be an ancestor of the giraffes of today. Once, they said, there had been none of the long-necked giraffes we all know, just the short-necked *Helladotherium.* But over a great period of time the *Helladotherium's* neck got longer—and longer—and longer—until there were no more animals like *Helladotherium,* because they had changed or *evolved* into giraffes.

Scientists believed that the *Helladotherium* must have died out far in the past. The long-necked giraffes were better able to find food, nibbling the tender leaves at the tops of trees—and so they flourished while their short-necked relatives became extinct.

Then, about 1900, there came a shock. In a remote part of Africa explorers found a shy, gentle animal that the natives called *okapi.* It looked a little like a horse, a little like a giraffe. The astonished scientists realized that a living *Helladotherium* had been discovered! The ancestor of the giraffe, thought to be long extinct, had survived down the ages in this one part of the world!

The story of the *Helladotherium* fossil and the surviving okapi tells us two important facts about living creatures, facts that will be illustrated again and again in the pages that follow.

One is that living things change as time passes. The changes do not happen rapidly, but bit by bit, the descendants of an okapi can be transformed by evolution into giraffes. It might take a million years and many million generations of okapis to bring about the change. Evolution is almost always gradual.

The other fact is that not every kind of animal undergoes such changes. Some survive, forgotten by time, in odd corners of the world. They have hardly changed at all over millions of years. We call such creatures *living fossils,* and we will meet a great variety of them in this book.

All of the curious creatures of Australia are living fossils—the kangaroo, the koala bear, the platypus, the wombat, and the rest of that unique tribe. The giant tortoise of the Galapagos Islands belongs in the living fossil group, as do the penguin, the armadillo, and the aardvark.

Not all living fossils are rare and strange, though. The cockroach has hundreds of millions of years of history behind him; so does that other household pest, the silverfish. These living fossils were ancient creatures when the first dinosaurs appeared. Crocodiles, alligators, and sharks, ostriches and opossums, horseshoe crabs, and the ginkgo trees that line our city streets—these are living fossils too.

New ones are discovered all the time. One of the most famous was found in 1938, when a fishing boat off the east coast of Africa pulled in a weird blue fish almost five feet long that looked like no fish anyone had ever seen before. An amazed expert identified it as a *coelacanth*—an extremely primitive kind of fish that was thought to have died out 70 million years ago. "It would have been less surprising," one scientist said, "to have caught a live dinosaur."

If the coelacanth had been discovered a hundred fifty years ago, however, it would have caused much less astonishment. In those days it was not surprising that creatures could survive unchanged from the beginning of time. That was what they were supposed to do. What was hard to believe, then, was that some kinds of plants and animals might die out or evolve into new types. The idea of change is very recent.

A few hundred years ago, no one knew of dinosaurs or coelacanths or okapis. Nor did people believe the world was ancient. In 1650, Archbishop James Ussher of the Irish city of Armagh published a book telling the age of the world. It had been created, he said, in 4004 B.C. He reached that figure by adding up the ages of everyone in the Bible from Jesus Christ back to Adam. A few years later, another learned man improved on Ussher's figure by calculating the exact day the world began: October 18, 4004 B.C.

Most people were willing to accept this date without questioning it. They accepted another idea also: that

God had created all the living creatures at the same time, and that whatever God had created would survive unchanged until the end of the world.

The trouble was that men kept digging up peculiar fossil bones that did not seem to belong to any known animal. Some were gigantic in size; others had unusual forms. How could they be explained?

Some scholars said they were "models of God's rejected works." Some argued that they were nothing but stones that had come to take the appearance of bones. Still others explained the big bones away by quoting the Biblical phrase, "There were giants in the earth in those days." They claimed that the monstrous skeletons belonged to long-gone heroes. In 1718, one wise man used fossil evidence to prove that Adam had been 125 feet 6 inches tall!

In time there was too much evidence to ignore. It no longer could be denied that the earth held the remains of many creatures that had become extinct. How could this be squared with the words of the Bible? Perhaps by saying that the extinct creatures had lived before the flood of Noah. According to Archbishop Ussher, the flood had taken place in 2349 B.C. Many kinds of animals had been wiped out by the deluge, said the scholars, and God had not created them a second time when the waters went down.

Again the evidence caused trouble. Men were carefully digging down and noticing the order of the fossil burials. An Englishman named William Smith discovered in 1791 that the rocks of the earth are arranged in definite layers, or *strata*. Each stratum contained certain types of fossils not found in other ones. And the simplest creatures, small sea animals, were found in the deepest strata. The closer to the surface, the more complicated the fossil animals were. Smith's work seemed to show that life had appeared in stages over a great span of time—first the simplest creatures, then more advanced ones like fish and frogs and lizards, and then the warm-blooded mammals last of all.

Once more the learned men tried to make the facts fit the Biblical story. It was necessary now to say there had been many floods and catastrophes, not just one. A nineteenth-century French zoologist named d'Orbigny said there had been at least *twenty-seven* worldwide catastrophes. After each one, God had brought new forms of life into being.

When explanations of scientific evidence get that complex, they start to look suspicious. By the time the nineteenth century was thirty years old, some scientists were proposing extremely daring new ideas. They said that the world was much older than the not quite 6,000 years Archbishop Ussher gave it. And they said that there was nothing sacred about the forms of living things. Creatures could change their appearances as time passed—or they might die out altogether.

A number of men put these ideas together, piece by piece. The one who brought all the pieces together into one solid structure was an eccentric, long-bearded, wealthy Englishman, troubled by headaches and a dislike of strangers, who was born the same day as Abraham Lincoln—February 12, 1809. His name was Charles Darwin. To him we owe the theory of evolution.

Darwin's father and grandfather had been doctors, but young Charles was a poor student and hated having to be near sick people. What interested him was natural history. He collected shells, plants, stones, and insects, and went for long walks in the countryside, studying all he saw. When he was twenty-two, he was invited to take part in a round-the-world scientific cruise aboard H.M.S. *Beagle*, which the British government was sending out for a five-year expedition. Darwin was signed on as the expedition's naturalist.

The *Beagle* went almost everywhere—to Brazil, then down the South American coast to Patagonia, into the Pacific and up the western coast of South America to Chile, and onward toward the coral islands of the South Pacific. Darwin collected many specimens of animals unknown to science. When he reached the Galapagos Islands, a group of dry, uninhabited dots of land off the coast of Ecuador, he found a whole wonderland of new species. The strangest were the giant Galapagos tortoises. But Darwin also noticed certain birds that were somewhat like those found on the South American mainland—only slightly different. He began to wonder if their long isolation on these remote islands had caused them to change.

For more than twenty years Darwin pondered his

theories in silence. He felt that animals and plants must evolve, that time changes them, that the primitive fossil creatures were extinct ancestors of modern life. He piled up a great quantity of proof of these changes.

He asked himself what caused evolutionary changes to happen. He could not answer that directly; not until long after Darwin's death did scientists find out the process of change. We know today that the pattern of a creature's shape is governed by microscopic factors called *chromosomes* and *genes,* which can be altered in many ways.

But Darwin was able to explain how the changes, once they happened, could become permanent. There is a struggle for existence, he said, and only the most fit survive. Those that are best equipped for meeting all the challenges of life are the ones that endure and pass their abilities on to their offspring.

One of Darwin's many examples was the giraffe. He did not know of the okapi, and worked from the evidence of fossils. Giraffes eat leaves. They browse on high branches, nibbling the tenderest greenery. Many other animals also eat leaves, so the lower branches of trees are often bare. Only a creature with a long neck can get to the untouched top branches.

Suppose, Darwin said, a giraffe were born with a neck slightly longer than that of any other giraffe. He would have an easier time reaching those top branches. That giraffe would grow plump and healthy and would have many offspring. Shorter-necked giraffes, competing with

each other for the sparse leaves on the lower branches, would go hungry. Some might starve to death; others would live, but would have few offspring. So a process of *natural selection* would breed a tribe of long-necked giraffes. Generation after generation, the giraffes with the longest necks would have the most offspring, and in time all giraffes would have very long necks indeed. (The long neck would not just be a way of reaching food, either. It would turn the giraffe into a kind of walking watchtower that could see enemies at a great distance—another help for survival.)

Darwin showed how natural selection weeded out the unfit and gave each living creature its distinctive form—the hooves of the horse, the fins of the fish, the trunk of the elephant, the intelligence of man. He finally published his book, *Origin of Species,* in 1859, and set off a hot debate that has still not fully ended.

Certain religious groups do not like Darwin's theories, because they do not seem to agree with the teachings of the Bible. At times the Soviet Union has objected to Darwin too, for various political reasons. But for most of us the theory of evolution is acceptable. It seems the best possible explanation for the evidence of the fossils in the rocks.

Time changes living things, then. But it does not change them all at the same rate.

We ourselves have changed extremely rapidly. A million years ago, our ancestors were short, small-brained, apish-looking creatures with low foreheads and weak chins. We have grown much taller, our skulls and teeth have acquired very different shapes, and our brains are twice as big as those of our many-many-great-grandfathers.

The fossil record of horses shows great change too, but not as fast. About 75 million years ago, the horse was a beast about the size of a medium-big dog, with four toes on the front feet and three on the back. This earliest horse, the *Eohippus,* or "dawn horse," lived in forests, browsing on leaves. But the climate changed, and forests gave way to open meadows and plains, where an ability to run was important for survival. The horse grew bigger and stronger, and its toes changed. The side toes became unimportant, and the center toe gained in size. We see fossils of three-toed horses, and then bigger horses with one large toe and two small splints beside it, and then still bigger horses with only the faint remnants of side toes, and finally the powerful, swift horse of today, with its strong hooves. The hoof, so the fossil record tells us, evolved out of that ever-bigger center toe.

Whenever circumstances force an animal to change or perish, evolution enters the picture. Some animals change rapidly—like human beings. Others, such as the horse, change a little less rapidly. Some are unable to evolve at all, and die out altogether. The dinosaurs are the most spectacular examples of animals that have become extinct.

The fossil record shows that there have been vast waves of extinction in the past. About 600 million years ago, the seas teemed with creatures known as *trilobites,* distant relatives of the lobsters and crabs of today. There were sixty different types of trilobites. Forty of those types died out almost at once, 100 million years later. The rest managed to survive in the changing conditions of the seas; but they, too, became extinct eventually. The last trilobite died some 300 million years ago.

After each wave of extinction, the creatures best fitted to continue remain to witness the next phase of evolution. The story of life is one of ever-growing complexity, but as each new family of beings comes on the stage, there are always a few survivors from the last act. These are the living fossils, overlooked by time.

Why do they survive while others fall into extinction?

There are many possible answers. Darwin, who coined the phrase *living fossil* when he wrote *Origin of Species,* declared, "They have endured to the present day from having inhabited a confined area, and from having been exposed to less varied, and therefore less severe, competition." That is, some creatures live in out-of-the-way places, where enemies are unable to reach them.

Others are naturally long-lived, and have many off-spring, so they are difficult to wipe out. Some are so tough and adaptable that they can withstand almost any change in their living conditions. As we make our tour through the world of the living fossils, we will see in detail how these survivors of an earlier time have managed to endure.

The living fossils give us a wider view of evolution than we might otherwise have. They are like boulders in the swiftly flowing river of time. By watching the water swirl and ripple around a boulder, we can get some idea of how fast the water is moving. The living fossils are our fixed points of reference. They have seen many forms of life come and go.

Living fossils themselves are of varying pedigrees, of course. Some go back almost to the beginning of life. Others made their appearance only a few million years ago. The newer ones are living fossils because they have survived while the rest of their group of era-mates has vanished. So the penguin, which goes back a mere 50 million years, is as much a living fossil as the sea lily, which has not changed for half a billion years.

Before we begin to look at our living fossils in detail, we'll need two road maps as our guides. One is a chart of the eras of the world's past, and the other is an outline of the family tree of the Animal Kingdom. (The plants have a family tree too, but it happens that most of the living fossils we will see are animals, so we'll save the sketch of plant evolution for a later chapter.)

The table of eras helps us to keep in mind just how old the earth really is. Very few people still agree with Archbishop Ussher that everything began in 4004 B.C. Scientists today think that the earth is between 3 and 5 *billion* years old. For most of that time, no life existed. The world was a ball of molten rock that cooled for

TABLE OF GEOLOGICAL ERAS

ERA	PERIOD	APPROXIMATE LENGTH	TYPICAL ANIMAL LIFE
HOLOCENE (RECENT)		Past 10,000 years	*Modern man*
QUATERNARY	Pleistocene	1,000,000 years	*Human and prehuman forms* *Large mammals*
CENOZOIC (TERTIARY)	Pliocene	12,000,000 years	*Manlike apes, sloths*
	Miocene	15,000,000 years	*Tapirs, first apes*
	Oligocene	10,000,000 years	*Monkeys, three-toed horses*
	Eocene	20,000,000 years	*Early hoofed mammals*
	Paleocene	12,000,000 years	*Small placental mammals*
MESOZOIC	Cretaceous	60,000,000 years	*Dinosaurs, marsupials*
	Jurassic	35,000,000 years	*Dinosaurs, first birds*
	Triassic	45,000,000 years	*Dinosaurs, earliest mammals*
PALEOZOIC	Permian	30,000,000 years	*First large reptiles*
	Pennsylvanian	20,000,000 years	*First reptiles, giant insects*
	Mississippian	30,000,000 years	*Amphibians*
	Devonian	60,000,000 years	*Coelacanths and other fish, first amphibians*
	Silurian	35,000,000 years	*First jawed fish, trilobites*
	Ordovician	75,000,000 years	*Trilobites, first jawless fish*
	Cambrian	90,000,000 years	*Trilobites*
PRE-CAMBRIAN (PROTEROZOIC, ARCHAEOZOIC)		2,000,000,000+ years	*First living creatures*

billions of years. In time, oceans appeared, and life started, we know not how, in the oceans. That was about 2 billion years ago.

The first living creatures were extremely simple—probably single-celled animals and plants like the protozoa and bacteria of today. Since they had no hard parts that could be preserved, we have no fossil evidence of these earliest living things. Then more complicated organisms appeared, such as seaweeds that left little skeletons of lime as fossils. Another life form found in rocks 2 billion years old is the *radiolarian*, a simple one-celled animal that built a delicate and lovely shell for itself out of silica. Many types of radiolarians still exist today, and they are not very different from the fossil ones of 2 billion years ago, so radiolarians are really our most ancient living fossils.

Radiolarian

Time passed—more time than we can begin to understand—and new kinds of animals appeared in the sea. Worms and sponges and corals, and then shellfish like the trilobites, and the ancestors of clams and lobsters and scorpions, all emerged as hundreds of millions of years passed. The first insects appeared, also. Then, about 400 million years ago, there came the first animals with backbones, the earliest fish.

Conditions changed; the warm seas grew colder, and the uninhabited land began to seem inviting. A few fish found ways of crawling out of the water and breathing air for a short while until they could get to another body of water. They scampered on their fins, which became thicker and sturdier in later generations, until the first amphibians developed—air-breathing animals with legs instead of flippers.

The amphibians still had to go back to the sea to lay their eggs, and they spent their first months in water, just as tadpoles do today before becoming frogs. Still later, the reptiles appeared, animals who remained on land through their whole life cycles. Some of these reptiles reached colossal bulk: the dinosaurs, we call them.

About 150 million years ago, while the vast dinosaurs were wallowing through their steaming tropic jungles, certain small animals of a different sort made their appearance. They were the mammals, who had fur instead of scales, produced milk to nourish their young, and differed from the reptiles in many other ways. The earliest mammals were probably egg-layers, but in time they began to bring their babies forth alive. Some mothers kept the newborn ones in pouches; these we call the *marsupials*. Others raised them in nests. Mammals grew bigger and more varied, while the dinosaurs vanished entirely. Another group of newcomers also appeared: the birds, among whom the reptilian scales had turned to feathers. And very late in the age of mammals, one fur-covered creature learned the trick of walking on his hind legs. Within a few million years he had progressed far enough to make himself master of the whole planet.

Scientists have divided the story of the earth and of living things into eras, subdivided into periods and epochs. It is important to remember that each of these eras, periods, and epochs refers to a huge length of time, and that the boundaries between one division and the next are loose ones. One period shades into the next, with a good deal of overlap. Also, the names we use are strictly for our own convenience. No dinosaur ever turned to his neighbor and said anything like, "It's January first, and we've just entered the Cretaceous Period. The Jurassic's over!"

As each new group of creatures appeared in turn, the earlier ones gave way, but did not die out altogether. Dinosaurs and trilobites became extinct, but some members of each reigning life form always remained—the living fossils, the debris left behind as time flows on. Cockroaches and dragonflies linger from the Permian, sea lilies from the Cretaceous, coelacanths from the Devonian, and so on.

Our other road map tells us the relation of one animal to another, by placing them in a kind of family tree. Again, this is strictly a man-made classification. It can be changed whenever new evidence turns up, and it has been so changed many times since it was first devised.

Putting animals in different pigeonholes may look easy, but when we try it the problems begin to crop up in a hurry. There are always exceptions to the general rules. We might begin by classifying animals that look like one another. All kinds of dogs, from poodles and Chihuahuas to Great Danes, look more like one another than they do like cats, horses, or elephants. So we can put all the dogs together, and all the cats, all the horses, all the elephants. But there are differences within the groups. Some elephants have bigger ears than others; some horselike creatures have black-and-white stripes. We have to subdivide our groups.

We get into trouble quickly if we make our groups too big. What if we tried to class all the animals that fly in one category? Birds, bats, insects—they all fly. But a beetle is not very much like a bat or a bird. And some birds do not fly at all, though otherwise they look like other birds.

How about animals that live in shells? Clams and oysters must be closely related, but what about snails? Lobsters have shells of a sort, and so do turtles. Do they all belong in the same class?

Scientists have been trying to classify animals and plants for hundreds of years now. The science of classification is called *taxonomy*, from the Greek word *taxis*, meaning "arrangement" or "order." Though he was by no means the first taxonomist, the most famous is Carl von Linné of Sweden (1707–1778), better known by his Latin name of Carolus Linnaeus. Linnaeus originated the idea of giving all living things scientific names, and arranged the various creatures in a careful order. The system used today is based on Linnaeus' work.

Taxonomists divide all life into two kingdoms, the Animal Kingdom and the Plant Kingdom. These kingdoms are divided into large groupings called *phyla,* from the Greek word meaning "race" or "tribe." Each phylum, next, is broken into classes, the classes into orders, the orders into families, the families into genera, and each genus into species and subspecies. The phylum we belong to is that of *Vertebrata,* or animals with backbones. Our phylum is divided into five classes: *Pisces* (fishes), *Amphibia* (cold-blooded animals that spend part of their lives in the water and part on land), *Reptilia* (cold-blooded air-breathers), *Aves* (birds), and *Mammalia* (warm-blooded milk-giving animals). The taxonomical classification of human beings looks like this:

KINGDOM—*Animal*
PHYLUM—*Vertebrata*
CLASS—*Mammalia*
ORDER—*Primates*
SUBORDER—*Anthropoidea*
FAMILY—*Hominidae*
GENUS—*Homo*
SPECIES—*Sapiens*

Our family tree is simpler than most because all

living human beings belong to the species *Homo sapiens.* The difference in color among humans is considered too minor to require setting up separate species. Once there were other species of the genus *Homo,* such as the stocky Neanderthal man of Ice Age days, but those species are all extinct.

Other animals are divided more finely. House cats and lions and tigers all belong to the genus *Felis,* but are of different species. The many kinds of pet dogs all belong to the species *Canis familiaris,* but the European wolf is *Canis lupus,* and the American timber wolf is *Canis occidentalis.*

The taxonomists often disagree. Some of them, for instance, think that all elephants belong in the same genus. They call the African elephant *Elephas africanus,* and the small-eared Indian elephant *Elephas maximus.* Others feel that the differences between the two kinds of elephants are so great that they should go, not simply into different species, but into different genera, and they call the African elephant *Loxodonta africanus.*

As we will see, living fossils often pose much tougher problems. Many of them are so different from all other creatures that it is hard to fit them into any known order, or even into any known phylum. Sometimes a living fossil will seem to overlap two phyla, such as the one known as *Peripatus,* which is like a worm in some ways and like an insect in others.

The chart of the Animal Kingdom will be useful in showing where taxonomists of today classify the many kinds of life. It will be most important to us in demonstrating where the living fossils do *not* fit in. The main phyla are:

PROTOZOA—*Simple one-celled animals.*

PORIFERA—*Sponges.*

COELENTERATA—*Corals and other hollow-bodied simple sea creatures.*

ECHINODERMA—*Spiny-skinned animals, such as sea urchins, starfish, and sea lilies.*

VERMES—*Worms.*

BRYOZOA—*So-called moss animals that live in large colonies and have hard horny coverings.*

BRACHIOPODA—*Animals with two shells of unequal size.*

MOLLUSCA—*A large phylum of creatures with shells, divided into three main classes:*

1. *Pelecypoda.* Two-shelled creatures with shells of equal size, such as clams and oysters.
2. *Gastropoda.* One-shelled creatures, such as snails.
3. *Cephalopoda.* Squids, octopuses, and several minor families.

ARTHROPODA—*The largest of all phyla in number of species, including all the jointed or segmented animals. It has three main divisions:*

1. *Crustacea.* Lobsters, crayfish, barnacles, crabs.
2. *Arachnida.* Spiders, scorpions.
3. *Insecta.* Insects.

VERTEBRATA—*Animals with backbones, divided into these classes:*

1. *Pisces.* Fishes.
2. *Amphibia.* Frogs, toads, salamanders.
3. *Reptilia.* Lizards, snakes, turtles, crocodiles, alligators.
4. *Aves.* Birds.
5. *Mammalia.* Mammals.

This is just the bare outline. A few extremely minor phyla have been omitted, as well as all extinct ones. And the sub-subdivisions have been left out. What we have is a basic picture of the Animal Kingdom from bottom to top, with ourselves, as the most complicated and most intelligent of all creatures, placed unhumbly at the summit of all creation. Most scientists believe that the order of phyla as it is given here is the order in which the different creatures evolved—the protozoa first and the mammals last, with the crustacea before the fish, the fish before the amphibia, the amphibia before the reptiles, and so on.

Equipped with our chart of eras and our outline of animal life, we can look now at some of the living fossils, the creatures forgotten by time.

Two: OUT OF THE SEA

LIFE BEGAN IN THE OCEANS. Through some miracle that we may never understand, chemical substances came together and took on the mysterious qualities we call life. They started to grow, to eat, to reproduce. Gradually the first extremely simple life forms became more complex, and the march of the phyla began.

When men came to make scientific observations in the world about them, they decided that although the upper layers of the sea were thickly populated, the depths must be lifeless. They lowered thermometers as deeply as they could and found that the water temperature dropped sharply where sunlight could not reach. Early in the nineteenth century, most scientists believed that the bottom of the sea must be a sheet of ice.

Then they began to dredge up living creatures from the abyss. In 1818, the British Arctic explorer Sir John Ross accidentally discovered a starfish at a depth of 4,900 feet while taking ocean measurements. Eighteen years later, another deep-sea dredge produced something more surprising: a primitive plantlike animal that was thought to have died out in the Mesozoic, when dinosaurs flourished. This was a crinoid, or sea lily. Fossil crinoids had often been unearthed, but no one had ever seen a live one before.

Crinoids

That first crinoid of 1836 went almost unnoticed by science. In 1850, though, a Norwegian pastor and zoologist named Michael Sars touched off real excitement when he went fishing for deep-sea creatures with his fifteen-year-old son Johan Ernst. From a depth of more than two thousand feet off the Lofoten Islands of Norway, father and son pulled a brittle, long-stemmed crinoid that resembled fossil sea lilies of the Mesozoic, 150 million years old. It looked like a plant, with its crown of five waving "leaves," but actually it was an animal about four inches tall that fed on smaller creatures unlucky enough to swim within its reach. It was given the scientific name of *Rhizocrinus lofotensis*, meaning "stalked crinoid from Lofoten."

Crinoids first appeared during the Ordovician Period, about 400 million years ago. They flourished and multiplied. By Silurian times there were more than 300 species, and in the Mississippian they were so numerous that they formed vast "gardens" in the ocean. The central part of North America was then covered by a shallow sea thronging with more than 400 kinds of sea lilies. Today, their skeletons form a fossil mass of limestone 200 to 500 feet thick, covering tens of thousands of square miles in the Mississippi Valley. But by the time the dinosaurs arrived, most crinoids were extinct.

Pastor Sars and his son went on finding crinoids and other strange relics of the past that were living comfortably in the "lifeless" sea. That caused a complete turnabout in scientific thinking. Men now declared that the sea must be a vast museum of ancient creatures. Many living fossils, they said, must survive undisturbed in the deeps.

The man who believed this most firmly was the Scottish naturalist Charles Wyville Thomson (1830–1882). Thomson was so excited by the Sars' discovery of crinoids that he devoted most of his adult life to studying these ancient animals. In 1862, he suggested that the British government sponsor an expedition to look for other deep-sea creatures. The government agreed, and for the next fifteen years Thomson roved the oceans, searching for living fossils.

His most famous expedition was the voyage of H.M.S. *Challenger*, from 1872 to 1876. The *Challenger* went round the world, lowering its dredges in many oceans. Up from the depths came crabs and worms, squids and octopuses, and bizarre, nightmarish deep-sea fish. Thomson found some more crinoids, too. Other naturalists were also discovering the five-armed creatures. One of them was Louis Agassiz, who was shown a sea lily brought up alive in the Caribbean in 1872. He wrote, "It was a very impressive sight for me to watch the movements of the creature, for it not only told of its own ways, but at the same time afforded a glimpse into the countless ages of the past, when these crinoids, so rare, and so rarely seen nowadays, formed a prominent feature of the animal kingdom."

Charles Wyville Thomson had expected to find a host of living fossils on the *Challenger* expedition. Much to his surprise and disappointment, he found very few. One of them was a type of crab known as an *eryonid*, which was a common fossil in Jurassic rocks 150 million years old. Then, eryonids had lived near the shore. Instead of becoming extinct, as everyone thought, these small pink crabs had gone to live in the deep sea off Africa, where Thomson found them with his dredges.

That was one accomplishment, though a small one. It matched Thomson's find on an earlier voyage of a large red sea urchin that supposedly had died out in the Cretaceous. But where were the many other ancient animals that should be lurking in the abyss? Thomson did not know. He came to realize that the deep sea did not contain many living fossils after all. In fact, the voyage

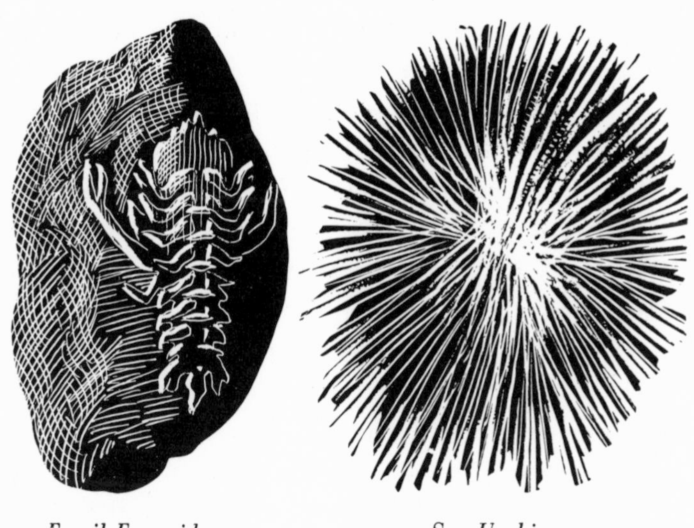

Fossil Eryonid *Sea Urchin*

of the *Challenger* removed one very celebrated living fossil from the list altogether.

This was *Bathybius haeckeli*—according to some, the oldest living fossil of them all.

The embarrassing story of *Bathybius* began about 1850. The German naturalist Ernst Haeckel suggested that life had begun in the sea, in the form of a kind of slime covering the ocean bottom. In 1857, the British ship *Cyclops* crossed the Atlantic collecting samples of the sea floor. These mud samples were brought up in iron tubes and placed in glass jars filled with alcohol to preserve any living things that might inhabit the mud.

With Haeckel's theory in mind, the English scientist Thomas Henry Huxley examined the mud samples from the *Cyclops*. Peering close, he spied a thin film of a jellylike slime smeared over the mud. Huxley, one of the greatest scientific figures of his day, was delighted. Here was Haeckel's original life form! The first kind of living thing had survived across the ages! He named it *Bathybius haeckeli*, in honor of his German colleague.

Charles Wyville Thomson and many other important men agreed that this gray ooze was the most ancient of living fossils, "the mother of life." Naturally, the *Challenger* scientists tried to discover new samples of *Bathybius*—and succeeded. The expedition's chemist, Dr. J. Y. Buchanan, studied the slime carefully and turned many faces red with his findings.

Bathybius, he showed, had never been alive at all. Any museum could produce some without the bother of dredging the sea's floor. Simply pour some alcohol into a jar of ocean water. A slime would form, consisting of calcium sulphate, a chemical that appeared when alcohol and ocean water were mixed. So much for *Bathybius!*

The quest for living fossils in the sea proved unsuccessful. There were many unusual forms of life in the abyss, but nearly all of them had evolved quite recently. The idea that the sea was a snug harbor for ancient creatures had to go into the discard. Pastor Sars had sounded a false alarm with his sea lilies.

Many scientific expeditions have followed the *Challenger*'s path, however. And a few living fossils have been brought from the water.

One of them is the strange cephalopod *Vampiroteuthis infernalis*, which a German biologist named Carl Chun discovered at the end of the last century. Cephalopods are mollusks. The best-known cephalopods are the squid and the octopus, and at first glance it may be hard to see how such large, active creatures are related to their fellow mollusks, the clam, the snail, and the oyster. What they have in common is their soft, boneless bodies, their rasping filelike organ that takes the place of teeth, and their shells. (A few mollusks don't have shells; there are always *some* exceptions!)

The word *cephalopod* comes from the Greek, and means "head-footed." The name refers to the arms or tentacles that surround a cephalopod's mouth. The earliest cephalopod fossils are about 400 million years old.

More than 10,000 species of cephalopods are known—90 percent of them extinct.

Carl Chun gave *Vampiroteuthis* its name because of its startling appearance. It would be a frightening beast if it were not just five to eight inches long. Jet black in color, with purplish tones, it has eight writhing tentacles, a pair of paddle-shaped fins, and two extra arms, long and slender, that tuck into special pockets of the body. A broad web links the eight ordinary tentacles. A good description of *Vampiroteuthis*, the "vampire octopus," comes from a book by the zoologist William Beebe. He told how he captured "a very small but very terrible octopus, black as night, with ivory white jaws and blood red eyes. This came along, half swimming, half sidling, its eight cupped arms all joined together by an ebony web."

When Carl Chun published the first report of *Vampiroteuthis,* he counted eight tentacles, and therefore called it an octopus. (*Octopus* is derived from Greek words meaning "having eight feet.") Then a close study turned up the two long extra arms. Cephalopods with ten tentacles are usually classed as squids. But the *second* pair of tentacles is longest among squids. In *Vampiroteuthis*, it is the fourth pair. And squids have suckers on their longest tentacles for catching food, but *Vampiroteuthis* does not. Those extra arms may be a kind of feelers, not used in hunting at all.

So the devilish-looking little cephalopod was neither an octopus nor a squid. It had to be placed in an order by itself. Its only known relatives live during the Cretaceous Period, at the height of the dinosaur era. There were many such creatures then—but all disappeared execept one.

Why did *Vampiroteuthis* survive?

Good luck, maybe, and skill at outwitting enemies. Living in the depths of the sea may have helped too. *Vampiroteuthis* hardly ever rises above a 3,000-foot depth, and spends most of its time twice as deep as that.

Vampiroteuthis

One scientific expedition caught a specimen at 9,850 feet.

Oddly, *Vampiroteuthis* has extremely large, keen eyes. This seems strange, for little light can reach such deep water, and eyesight is not usually very useful in a world of near-total darkness. Possibly *Vampiroteuthis'* eyes are so sensitive that they can see even in the faintest greenish flicker of light.

In 1952, a Danish scientific expedition aboard the ship *Galathea* pulled in a much more unusual living fossil that startled the scientific world—*Neopilina.*

Neopilina certainly does not look very startling at first glance. It seems to be a limpet, one of those flattened, cap-shaped shelled creatures that can be found clinging tightly to rocks at many seashores. Limpets are mollusks of the class called *Gastropoda,* which also includes the snails, periwinkles, and whelks. All these creatures have a single shell (unlike clams, for instance, which have two), a fleshy foot used for clinging and walking, a toothed tongue, and gills.

Neopilina—top

The creature now known as *Neopilina* was caught at a depth of two miles off the west coast of Mexico in 1952. Looking at the flat, thin-shelled mollusk, only about two inches in diameter, its discoverers thought it was just some new kind of deep-sea limpet. Only after careful study did they discover how unusual it really was.

Though mollusklike in general appearance, *Neopilina* turned out to be faintly divided into a number of distinct body segments. Mollusks are not *supposed* to be segmented. That body design is considered an extremely primitive trait. It is found in the phylum one notch lower than mollusks, that of worms. It is also found one phylum up from mollusks, in the arthropods, the phylum of lobsters, crabs, insects, and spiders. *Neopilina* had another arthropod feature, too—its gills, kidneys, and muscles were arranged in pairs. So it seemed to belong to three possible phyla.

That was what was so bewildering when Dr. Henning Lemche of Copenhagen finally announced the find in 1957. He had waited five years from the time the

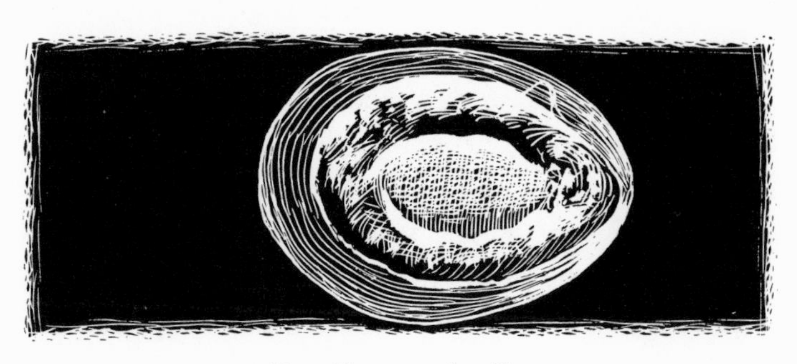

Neopilina—underside

Galathea had pulled the puzzling animal from its home on the dark, muddy clay of the sea floor. After careful study, Dr. Lemche decided that the *Galathea* had found an amazing living fossil—an animal that went back unchanged to a time so remote it numbed the mind. It was almost identical to a fossil called *Pilina,* which had been extinct more than 350 million years. So he called it "new *Pilina,*" *Neopilina,* giving it the species name of *galatheae* in honor of the ship.

The "old" *Pilina* belonged to a group called the *monoplacophorans,* which flourished when the divisions between the phyla were not as great as they are today. Many different tribes of animals sprang from such forms, each going its own evolutionary way. Exactly where the monoplacophorans fit into the family tree is hazy; they seem to be worms on the way to becoming mollusks, but they have arthropod features as well. One writer has called them "worm snails" and let it go at that. They are connecting links between several animal groups now widely separated. That was why the British biologist Dr. C. M. Yonge called *Neopilina*'s discovery "a zoological event of the first order" that in itself made the voyage of the *Galathea* round the world worth while!

The fragile "worm snail" is rather attractive. Its shell is almost transparent, yellowish-white on the outside, coated with shining mother-of-pearl within. When the shell is turned over the animal itself can be seen. Most of it is a large, round foot, bluish with a pink area in the center. Five pairs of gills surround the foot.

In 1958, soon after the first *Neopilina* was publicly discussed, the research ship *Vema* found more specimens off the coast of northern Peru. These were living much deeper, more than 19,000 feet down. They were different in minor ways from the first type. Probably other *Neopilinas* will be discovered by later expeditions. They will keep scientists busy for years, as they struggle to understand the path evolution took in developing the mollusks. Having twentieth-century *Neopilinas* to study is something like having a time machine that peers back half a billion years.

Three: THE JOINTED-LEGGED ONES

HUMAN BEINGS ARE VAIN ABOUT their place in the world. They like to think of themselves as masters of everything—and, in most ways, they are. But when it comes to real success as living creatures, we have to look toward the arthropods.

There are more different species of arthropods than of all other kinds of animals put together. Three fourths of all known species belong in the phylum of jointed-legged animals. That phylum takes in the insects, spiders, scorpions, lobsters, shrimps, crabs, fleas, centipedes, barnacles, ticks, mites, and many, many others. Flying, swimming, crawling—arthropods are all about us. And they have been here a long time. From the viewpoint of the cockroach tribe, mammals arrived on earth only a moment ago, and the dinosaurs vanished just the other day.

Arthropods, like the worms a couple of phyla below them, have segmented bodies. But they have developed far beyond the worms, growing hard, horny coats of armor. The shell of a lobster or the tough skin of an ant is actually the animal's skeleton, worn outside the body instead of within. All the muscles and soft tissues of the arthropod's body are attached to this skeleton-on-the-outside. Another important feature of the arthropods is the jointed form of the legs. *Arthropod* means just that—"having jointed legs."

Because arthropods have hard coverings, they are often preserved in fossil form. Some have been embedded in sticky drops of resin given off by ancient pine trees; others have left molds of their bodies in sand or mud that hardened to rock during endless ages. From the fossil record, we know that many kinds of arthropods have survived almost unchanged over hundreds of millions of years. It is a phylum full of living fossils, and we can discuss only a few.

One of them is common along the Atlantic shore of the United States, and is found in one other part of the world far away, the East Indies. It is *Limulus*, the horseshoe crab, whose fossil remains go back at least 250 million years.

The horseshoe crab *looks* like something from a different age. It has a dome-shaped shell with the general outline of a horseshoe. A thick, wicked-looking spike sticks out behind the shell like a sword. As it crawls slowly along the sandy beach, the horseshoe crab seems to be a strange armored tank or perhaps an invader from

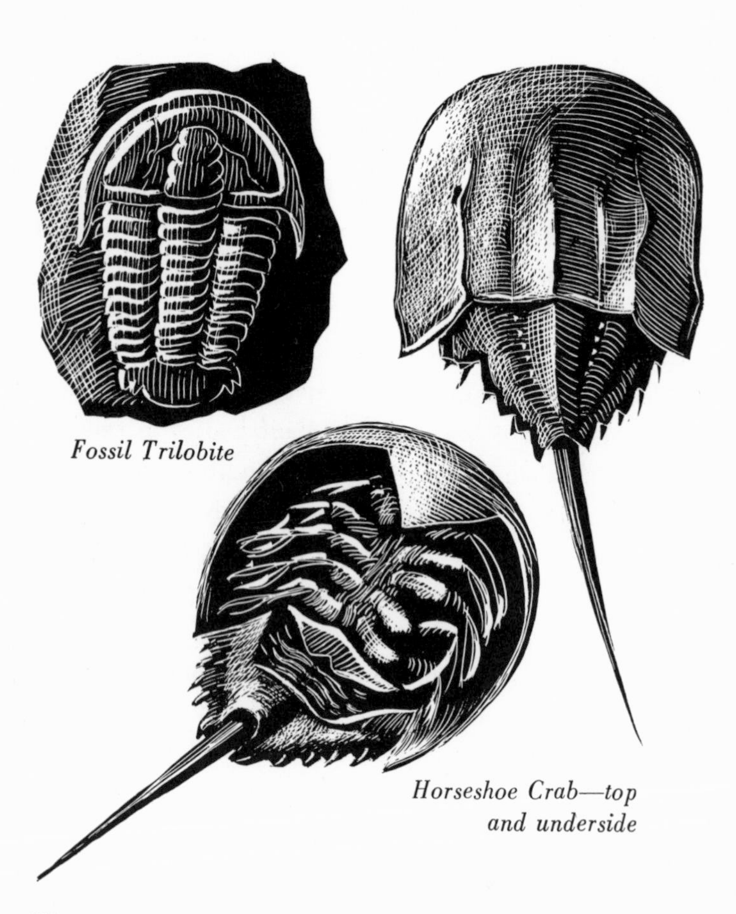

Fossil Trilobite

Horseshoe Crab—top and underside

another world. Underneath there are six pairs of legs, with the mouth located in their midst, and smaller legs behind them which are used in swimming. The biggest horseshoe crabs are about two feet long.

Horseshoe crabs are found in great numbers, so they are obviously good survivors. In the last century, they were ground up and used for fertilizer, and in 185 more than a million of them were captured in a one-mile stretch of New Jersey beach. Despite such heavy hunting, they seem to be still plentiful in the Atlantic today.

One of the first to describe *Limulus* was the English mathematician Thomas Harriott, who was part of a pioneering settlement in Virginia in 1585. About a hundred years later the East Indian variety came to light, thanks to a Dutch businessman named Georg Eberhard Rumpf, who used the Latin name of Rumphius in his writings. Rumphius was a soldier in his youth, and fought in the Dutch army against the Portuguese when those two countries were struggling for control of Southeast Asia. When he was about thirty, Rumphius became a merchant and settled on the island of Amboina in what is now Indonesia. His hobby was natural history, and he collected specimens of many native animals. Among them was that many-armed cephalopod, the nautilus, and the horseshoe crab.

Rumphius began to go blind in 1670, and had to retire from active life. He spent the next twenty years dictating a great book on natural history to a secretary. The manuscript was destroyed by fire in 1687, and old

Rumphius had to write it all over, a task that took several years. In 1692, he packed up his manuscript and sent it to Amsterdam to be printed at last—and the ship carrying it was lost at sea. Luckily, an admirer of Rumphius had gone to the great expense of making a copy, and that, with its description of the horseshoe crab, finally reached the printer shortly before Rumphius' death in 1702.

Nowhere else in the world have horseshoe crabs been found. Many thousands of miles separate the eastern shore of the United States from the islands of Indonesia. Why *Limulus* survives in only those two regions is a mystery beyond our solving. Once, when most of the world was covered by water, horseshoe crabs lived in every sea. Some of the best fossil specimens have come from Germany and Austria, which were under water during the Jurassic and Triassic.

The horseshoe crab, strange to say, is not really a crab at all. Tip one over and it certainly looks crablike, its many jointed feet waving and thrashing indignantly. But true crabs have two pairs of antennae, or feelers. *Limulus* has only one pair, and since its feelers bear claws, they really should be considered an extra set of legs. There are other differences of body structure that show that the horseshoe "crab" does not belong in the class of arthropods called *Crustacea*. Some taxonomists think it is more closely related to the arachnids (the spiders and scorpions). Others keep it in a class of its own. Like so many of the living fossils, the horseshoe crab is difficult to fit into one of the regular categories.

The best clue to its place in the scheme of things comes from studying its young ones. There are plenty of those, for the female horseshoe crab lays about ten thousand eggs at a time during the mating season of May and June. It takes about a month for the greenish-blue eggs to hatch, and what comes forth does not look much like an adult horseshoe crab. There is no tail spike, and the rear half of the body is divided into three sections or lobes, which are not visible in the adult.

What a baby *Limulus* resembles, in fact, is the extinct three-lobed arthropod known as the *trilobite.* In the Cambrian Period, trilobites were the lords of their world. There were hundreds of different kinds, some just a quarter of an inch long, others the size of a modern horseshoe crab. All had the three-lobed body pattern, but they varied widely otherwise. Some had the spiked tails of the horseshoe crab. One fanciful-looking trilobite, which reached a length of more than two feet, had *eight* spiked tails!

Real trilobites died out hundreds of millions of years ago, and we cannot call the horseshoe crab a true living trilobite. Though its young resemble trilobites closely, the three-lobed appearance is lost when the horseshoe crab matures. Perhaps *Limulus* is not only a living fossil in its own right, with 300 million years of changelessness behind it, but also the descendant of those earlier arthropods, altered by evolution but still keeping trilobite traits in babyhood.

Why has *Limulus* stopped evolving?

Actually, it hasn't. There have been small changes in its shape over those 300 million years, and the species that Thomas Harriott found in Virginia is slightly different from the one Rumphius caught in the waters off Amboina. But by normal standards the horseshoe crab seems immune to evolution. Why?

Because, apparently, it has reached a point where it is perfectly suited for getting along without further change. Its tough shell protects it from most enemies. It spends most of its time rooting in the mud, feeding on small mollusks and worms. It moves slowly and usually goes unnoticed and undisturbed. It has few real enemies, aside from the very recent breed of human beings who grind them up to make fertilizer and pig feed. And it lays many eggs at a time, so there are always plenty of young to continue the family. Quite possibly these spike-tailed little tanks with many jointed legs will still look as they do today when mankind has long since evolved into some unknown new form.

In another class of arthropods, the *Insecta,* we find some of the most common living fossils—cockroaches, silverfish, and dragonflies. Insects are six-legged creatures whose bodies are generally divided sharply into three sections, called the head, thorax, and abdomen. Many but not all insects have wings. All have the jointed legs that make them part of the arthropod phylum.

There are three main groups of insects. The most

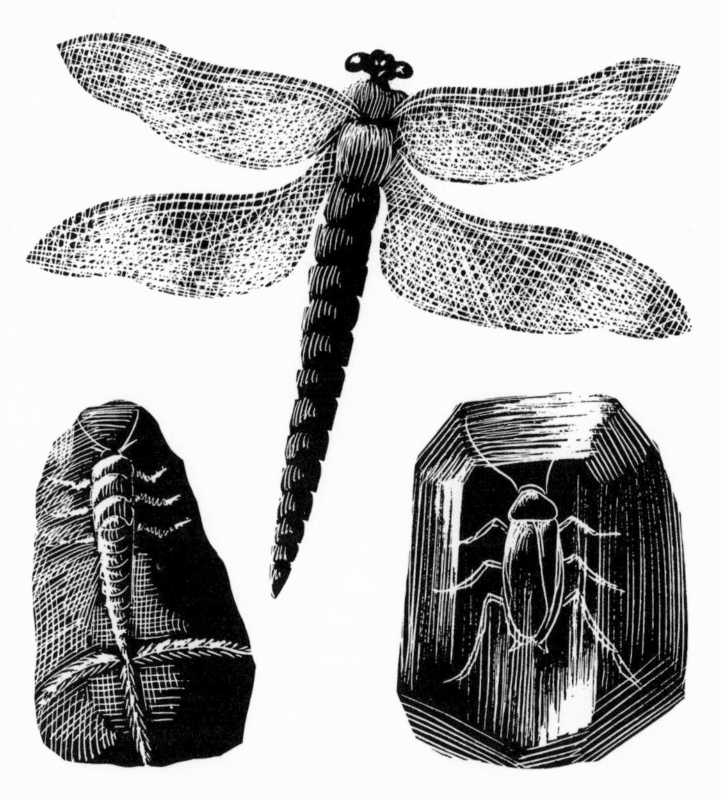

Fossil Silverfish *Dragonfly* *Cockroach in Amber*

primitive of these is the *Apterygota,* wingless insects whose fossil histories go back more than 250 million years. In a way, all the insects of this group can be called living fossils. They include such tiny, little-known insects as the bristletails and springtails, which live in decaying leaves of forests, on the surface of lakes and ponds, and even on the frozen wastes of Antarctica.

One member of this group has taken up residence in

the houses of human beings. This is the silverfish, which can sometimes be seen scurrying along the floor late at night. (They stay out of sight in the daytime.) Silverfish are long and narrow, with shining silvery-white bodies and yellowish legs. They have two feelers on their heads and three threadlike tails in back, and are about half an inch long, including feelers and tails. Microscopic shiny scales cover their bodies, giving them their silvery gleam. Silverfish appear to have a lifetime of several years, which is unusually long for such a small insect. A long life span for the individual animal seems to be part of the recipe for becoming a living fossil. As we will see, many other living fossils are extremely long-lived as individuals, not only as species.

No matter how long a cockroach lives, it is *too* long for the lady of the household. Housewives should be pleased, though, that the present-day members of that clan are only dwarf versions of their ancient ancestors. In the Pennsylvanian Period, at a time when much of the world was a hot tropical jungle, there were more than 800 species of cockroaches, and some of them were four to six inches in length.

Cockroaches belong to the second group of insects, the *Exopterygota.* Other members of this group are the locusts, crickets, termites, praying mantises, and dragonflies. What they all have in common is the presence of undeveloped wings that can be seen on the outside of the body at all stages of growth.

Though most of the giant forms of cockroach have

died out, the species that remain can be seen in fossil specimens as well as in dark corners of the kitchen. During the Pennsylvanian Period, it was the most common type of insect, and has held on through hundreds of millions of years despite the rise of newer forms of life. Also common in the Pennsylvanian were dragonflies with thirty-inch wingspreads, not very different except in size from those of today.

The third group of insects is called the *Endopterygota*. It includes beetles, ants, wasps, flies, mosquitoes, butterflies, and many other kinds of insects. In this group the undeveloped wings remain within the body and do not become visible until the adult stage is reached. Scientists believe that these insects emerged much later than those of the other two groups, although they are by no means newcomers themselves. There are no living fossils among them that compare in antiquity with the cockroach, the silverfish, and the dragonfly.

Since it has a great many more than six legs, the centipede cannot be called an insect. This arthropod is insect-like in most other ways, though. It rates being called a living fossil because its story goes back some 400 million years to the Silurian Period. The many-legged creatures may have been the first forms of life that left the sea to dwell permanently on land.

The word *centipede* means "having a hundred feet," but not many centipedes are so exact about it. One species has 173 pairs of legs, another has only 15; the average is about 35 pairs. A closely related group, the millipedes ("thousand-footed"), has even more legs—sometimes as many as 350 pairs. Centipedes feed upon insects and worms; they are fast-moving and rather fierce, many of them equipped with poison fangs. Millipedes are much slower creatures, despite their extra ration of legs, and feed on leaves and bark. These two families are often classed together as *myriapods,* meaning "having many feet." The largest known myriapods are certain tropical millipedes that reach a length of ten inches.

Myriapods, like horseshoe crabs, seem suited for a long stay in our world. They are rugged, and are found in hot countries and cold ones, in deserts and in swamps. Changes in the weather do not bother them at all. Centipedes are able to protect themselves against natural enemies through their speed and their poison fangs, while millipedes, living hidden under stones or bark, make themselves hard to find. Myriapods lay many eggs and coat them with a sticky substance that causes earth to stick to them. This provides a kind of camouflage that shields the eggs from harm. Possibly these are some of the reasons why the many-legged ones, who may have

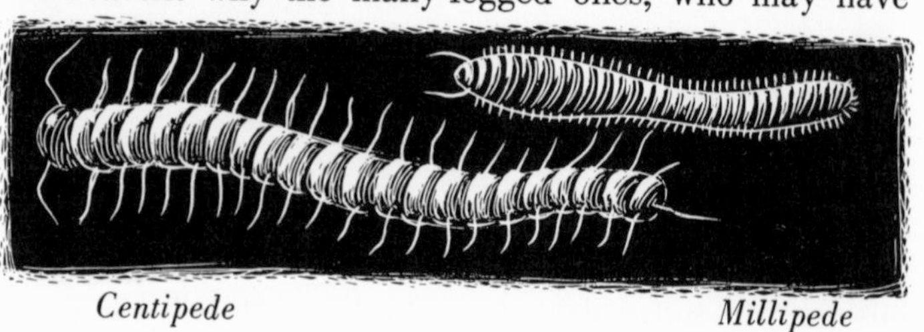

Centipede *Millipede*

been the first to quit the ancient seas, are still with us after hundreds of millions of years.

The last of our array of many-legged creatures is not exactly an arthropod, though it has some arthropodlike features. It looks something like a worm, but worms move on bristles, not on legs, so it doesn't quite fit into that phylum either. Some scientists think it is a wormlike arthropod. Some think it is an arthropodlike worm. Others put it in a phylum all by itself, the *Onychophora*, "claw-bearing ones." Its name is *Peripatus*, and it is possibly a missing link between the phylum of worms and the phylum that includes insects and other arthropods.

The first known *Peripatus* was discovered in 1825 by the Reverend Lansdown Guilding of the Caribbean island of St. Vincent. Like many island parsons, he made a hobby of natural history. When he came upon an odd sluglike creature as thick as a pencil and about three inches long, with thirty-three pairs of unjointed legs and two hornlike antennae on its head, he suspected he had something new.

The Reverend Mr. Guilding rushed an account of his discovery to London, where it was published in the January 1826 number of the *Zoological Journal*. Just how wrong he was about its nature can be guessed from the title of his article: "An Account of a New Genus of Mollusca." He thought that it was a kind of snail without a shell, and named it *Peripatus*, from the Greek word meaning "the wandering one." Today some eighty different species of *Peripatus* are known. They range in length from an inch and a half to about four inches, and the number of legs varies from fourteen to forty-three pairs. Their color range is just as wide—dark green, nearly black, to brown or reddish-orange. One species, which lives only in caves, is white.

Peripatus looks very much like a large caterpillar with soft, velvety skin. (The caterpillar, of course, is simply the young form of the butterfly or moth, and *Peripatus* is not closely related to those insects.) Each of the many legs of *Peripatus* ends in a small claw. It is a surprisingly attractive creature. Adam Sedgwick, a famous English geologist of the nineteenth century, had high praise for this little wanderer: "The exquisite sensitiveness and constantly changing form of the antennae, the well-rounded plump body, the eyes set like diamonds on the side of the head, the delicate feet, and, above all, the rich coloring and velvety texture of the skin, all combine to give these animals an aspect of quite exceptional beauty."

After the first *Peripatus* was found, naturalists searched for others, slowly adding to the list of known types. *Peripatus* is widespread, living in the tropical forests of Africa, Asia, Australia, South America, and Central America. But it prefers to hide in moist places on the forest floor, under stones or rotting logs, and finding it is not easy.

As scientific knowledge grew, it became obvious that

Pastor Guilding had been wrong to call *Peripatus* a mollusk. It was not closely related to snails and slugs at all. The classifiers tried to group it with the centipedes and millipedes, but that did not work. Bracketing it with the worms was even worse. *Peripatus* was not quite a worm, not quite an arthropod.

Its body showed no outward sign of segmentation. That was why Pastor Guilding had classed it as a mollusk, for mollusks are not segmented, but worms and arthropods are. However, *Peripatus* turned out to have segments under its velvety skin, and there was one segment for each pair of legs. The presence of legs removed *Peripatus* from the phylum of worms. Because the legs were unjointed, *Peripatus* could not be called an arthropod. It simply did not fit anywhere. Its system of blood circulation was like that of an arthropod. Its digestive system was more like that of a worm. Its brain was even less developed than that of a worm. *Peripatus* had to be some sort of living fossil, a survivor from an era when worms and insects were more similar than they are now.

In 1911, a fossil "worm" came to light that eventually explained some of the *Peripatus* mystery. Charles D. Walcott, an American fossil expert, found the fossil imprint of a many-legged wormlike creature near the mountain named Ayshea in the Canadian province of British Columbia. He called it *Aysheaia pedunculata*, "stalk-footed animal from Ayshea." The fossil was found in rocks dating from the Middle Cambrian Period —about 450 million years old.

Before long, someone thought of connecting *Aysheaia* with *Peripatus*. In 1930, Dr. George E. Hutchinson of Yale University studied *Peripatus* and the fossil that resembled it, and declared that *Aysheaia* was almost certainly the ancestor of the small puzzler.

Not that the two looked exactly alike. *Aysheaia* had fewer legs and body segments, slightly different claws, and its mouth was in the front of the body, not underneath, as in *Peripatus*. When *Aysheaia* lived, there were no land animals at all. It inhabited the warm shallow seas of its day. The changes worked by evolution in *Peripatus* had been just enough to transform it from a water-dweller to a forest-dweller. Otherwise the animal had changed very little since Cambrian times.

What are the special features that have allowed *Peripatus* to survive so long?

Like the millipedes, it keeps out of harm's way, down in the rotting leaves and twigs of the forest floor. It eats small insects, dead or alive, and has been known to tackle such large ones as dead grasshoppers. Thus there

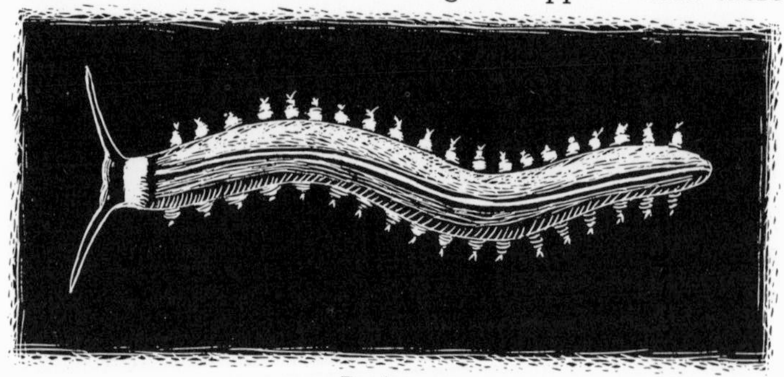

Peripatus

is always a steady supply of food. It protects its young ones well; instead of laying eggs, which would be at the mercy of any passing foe, most species of *Peripatus* bring forth their offspring alive and fully developed. *Peripatus* is armed for self-defense, too. When disturbed, it squirts a gluey substance from two nozzles beside its mouth. It can spray this as far as twelve inches, snaring any attacker about its own size. Lastly, each individual *Peripatus* lives many years.

All these are useful for long survival. But there is one peculiar feature of *Peripatus* that makes its whole story improbable. Common sense tells us that *Peripatus* really should have become extinct ages ago, because it is poorly equipped to deal with changes in its surroundings.

Peripatus breathes through air tubes connecting its skin with its inner tissues. Insects have these air tubes also; worms do not, because they can "breathe" with all parts of their skins. Insects, however, are able to close their air tubes during times of dryness. This prevents water from evaporating out of the body. Curiously, the

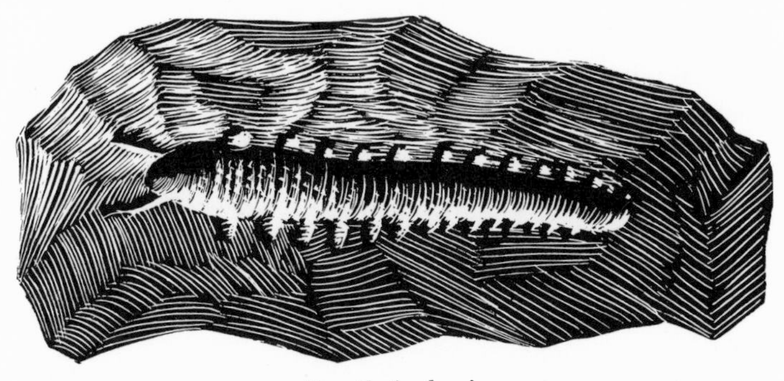

Fossil Aysheaia

Peripatus has no way of shutting its air tubes. So long as it remains in a damp place, that does not matter. But when the surroundings become dry, the body water of *Peripatus* is quickly lost. A *Peripatus* taken from its moist tropical home literally dies from evaporation in a short while. Placed in an ordinary dry room, it will lose a third of its body weight in less than four hours by giving off water. It will dry up twice as fast as an earthworm and forty times as fast as a caterpillar of the same size.

Peripatus' air tubes put it in an awkward position, halfway between worm and insect and worse off than either. Since climate changes as time passes, *Peripatus* should have been caught and wiped out as its dwelling places dried up. Somehow it defied logic and managed to find new homes damp enough for comfort.

It is a true relic of the past. It tells us of a time more than 500 million years ago when certain small creatures of the sea were beginning to take different evolutionary paths.

One group evolved into the worms. Another group grew jointed legs and became the arthropods. But a third faction scarcely changed at all, except to leave the sea for life on the not-too-dry land. This very primitive group has clung to existence ever since, watching the centuries go by from its hiding place under the rotting logs of tropical jungles.

Four: THE FINNY FOSSILS

THREE DAYS BEFORE CHRISTMAS 1938, a fishing trawler docked at the port of East London, South Africa. The river Chalumna reaches the sea at East London, and the shore dips gently where the river ends, forming a shelf about ten miles wide. The water is shallow there, and the fishing is good.

The trawler had had a fine trip and came back loaded with fish. Most of its catch was sharks. But the vessel had pulled in one unusual fish about four and a half feet long, a beautiful deep blue in color. It had been lively when caught, even trying to bite the captain's hand, but it died before it could be brought to shore. Since it seemed so strange, the trawler's captain telephoned Miss M. Courtenay-Latimer, who was in charge of the East London Museum, and told her of his find.

She hurried to the docks. The fish mystified her. Its mouth was huge; its scales were also large; its fins, instead of sprouting right from the body, were set on odd stumpy stalks that looked almost like the beginnings of legs. It weighed 127 pounds—and, in the African heat, it was already starting to decay.

The one man who might know something about the unknown fish was Professor J. L. B. Smith. He was a chemistry instructor at Rhodes University in Grahamstown, South Africa, but one of his part-time pursuits was ichthyology, the study of fishes. Professor Smith knew more about the fishes of the ocean off South Africa than anyone else. Miss Courtenay-Latimer set down a description of the fish, made a sketch of it, and wrote to Smith asking for his help.

Professor Smith was away on his Christmas holiday. The letter did not reach him for several weeks. Meanwhile the fish continued to decay, and Miss Courtenay-Latimer had no way of preserving it. She had to throw the flesh and inner organs away. The skin and bones were mounted.

When he got the letter, Professor Smith looked at the sketch and immediately recognized the fish. It was a *coelacanth* (pronounced SEE-la-kanth). But coelacanths

Coelacanth

had died out at the end of the Cretaceous Period, about 70 million years ago. And they had been small fish, five to twenty inches in length, nowhere near the size of this specimen. Could the fishing trawler possibly have snared a live coelacanth of great size? "Such things can't happen," Professor Smith told himself.

All the same, he hurried to East London to see Miss Courtenay-Latimer's stuffed fish. As he wrote later: "That first sight hit me like a white-hot blast and made me feel shaky and queer; my body tingled. I stood as if stricken to stone. Yes, there was not the shadow of a doubt, scale by scale, bone by bone, fin by fin, it was a true coelacanth."

Scientists throughout the world were surprised beyond words. Even laymen were caught up in the excitement, because the story made headlines in many newspapers. Few people had heard of coelacanths before, of course. But it was easy to grasp the importance of the discovery. Coelacanths were much older than the dinosaurs. They were thought to have vanished untold millions of years ago. Now, here was a live one turning up off the South African coast, like an ambassador from the Cretaceous! Never before or since has the finding of a living fossil caused such an uproar.

Coelacanths were not quite the first fish the world had known. The very first, we think, were animals called *ostracoderms,* meaning "armored skins." Ostracoderms were only a few inches long, with scaly tails, and plates of bone covering their heads and front parts. They had no fins, but did all their swimming with their tails. Instead of jaws, they had round or oval mouths equipped with movable bony plates. They fed by swimming along the bottom, digging in the mud for small animals.

These ostracoderms appeared in the Devonian Period, more than 350 million years ago. They were more advanced than the trilobites and other forms of life that already existed, because they had backbones. The backbones gave them a strength and a flexibility that mollusks and arthropods could not have.

Evolution took the ostracoderms on many paths. One group branched off and became the sharks, developing jaws and fins and losing their armor. The sharks did not have real bones. Their skeletons were—and still are—made from a soft material called cartilage.

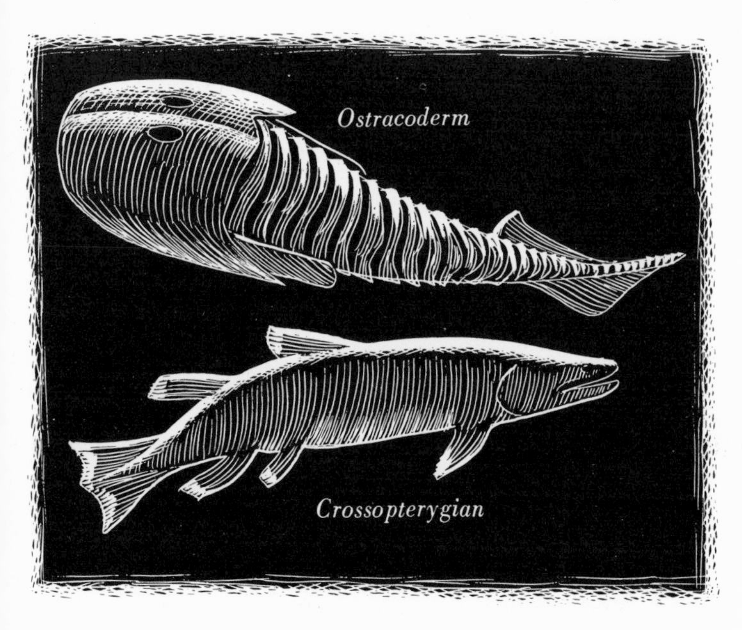

A second branch of the fish family also developed fins and jaws, but kept their bony armor as well. These were the *placoderms,* which soon became extinct. A third line led to the fishes of today, with fins, jaws, bony skeletons, and no protective plates of armor on the outside. The fourth branch was the coelacanth line.

This last group had fins set on stalks or lobes. Such fins looked like small paddles with soft fringes at one end. Scientists call them the *crossopterygians,* from the Greek words for "fringe" and "fin." In English they are known as the "lobe-finned fishes," but the German name, *Quastenflosser,* is more accurate. It means "tassel-finned."

The bones of those thick, sturdy fin-stalks are similar to the bones of arms and legs in land animals. A crossopterygian's fins were almost flippers. They seem strong enough to have allowed the fish to walk on the land.

That was exactly what one branch of the crossopterygian family eventually learned how to do. These fish, the *rhidipistians,* hauled themselves out of the sea. The late Devonian Period was a time of frequent drought in many parts of the world; lakes and ponds shrank or dried up completely. Perhaps those pioneering rhidipistians scrambled out of their drying lakes and crawled with great effort on their fins until they reached some bigger body of water, where they could swim more freely. But in time they lived more and more on land, until they evolved into the four-legged, air-breathing animals called amphibians, which lived in the water only while young. And in turn amphibians evolved into reptiles, reptiles into mammals, and one kind of mammal into human beings. So we can trace our family tree back to those fringe-finned fish of the Devonian Period!

Does that mean that the coelacanth is one of man's earliest ancestors?

No, because while the rhidipistians were crawling onto the land, the coelacanths were content to remain behind in the sea. They never evolved further in the direction of land life. As Professor Smith's wife once remarked, the coelacanth is "only a cousin of an ancestor of ours." It is the rhidipistian branch of the crossopterygians that we must call our ancestor.

So far as anyone knew up till 1938, the coelacanths were thoroughly extinct. The first fossil specimens had been found in England in 1840. Other species followed, and they were all grouped as coelacanths, meaning "hollow-spined fishes." One treasure trove of fossil coelacanths was uncovered some years ago in New Jersey when Princeton University was building a new library. The excavations revealed hundreds of 180-million-year-old coelacanth skeletons packed a dozen to the square foot in the rock.

Then, from South Africa, came the thunderbolt of the living coelacanth! Since it was much larger than any of the fossil forms, Professor Smith considered it a new species. He named it *Latimeria chalumnae,* to honor the young museum curator and to identify the Chalumna River's mouth as the place where the coelacanth had been caught. (After the Second World War, a fossil coelacanth as large as Miss Courtenay-Latimer's was unearthed in West Germany.)

Professor Smith was delighted to have a stuffed coelacanth to study, but now he wanted a complete one—if possible, one that was still alive. He felt certain that there must be other coelacanths lurking in the waters off East Africa. So he had thousands of leaflets printed, and handed them out to fishermen in the countries along the African coast. Written in English, Portuguese, and French, the leaflet showed a photograph of the mounted specimen. It offered a reward of £100, then about $400, for each of the first two coelacanths anyone might catch.

The leaflet said:

"Look carefully at this fish. It may bring you good fortune. . . . The only one ever saved for science was 5 ft. long. Others have been seen. If you have the good fortune to catch or find one DO NOT CUT IT OR CLEAN IT IN ANY WAY but get it whole at once to a cold storage plant. . . ."

Then Professor Smith waited for a telegram that would tell him a new coelacanth had been caught. He had to wait almost fourteen years. Just before Christmas 1952, he got a wire from a schooner skipper named Eric Hunt. Hunt had taken Smith's leaflets to the Comoro Islands, which lie between Madagascar and the mainland of Africa. "HAVE SPECIMEN COELACANTH FIVE FEET . . . ," Hunt wired.

A Comoro fisherman, Ahmed Hussein, had pulled a hundred-pound coelacanth out of the sea a few days before. The fish gave him a hard fight, and refused to die even after he had hauled it into his boat. He had to bash it on the head with a stick to kill it. Ahmed Hussein then took his prize to the market to sell for food. Another native fisherman recognized it as the twin of the fish whose photograph was on Professor Smith's leaflet. Together they hauled the coelacanth twenty-five miles over hills and valleys to Eric Hunt, whose schooner was in harbor on the island's north shore. He bought the fish and sent the telegram to Professor Smith. Hunt did not have a refrigerator big enough to hold it, so he packed the coelacanth in salt and injected it with formalin, which would keep it from decaying, as the first one had done.

Professor Smith hurried to the Comoro Islands. Getting there was no easy chore. Smith telephoned government officials, hoping they would give him the use of a military plane. He had to go right to the top—to Prime Minister Daniel Malan. The Prime Minister was a student of ichthyology also. He ordered a government plane to take Professor Smith to the Comoros at once.

When he arrived, he was too nervous to unwrap the fish himself. Someone else had to do it for him. A big blue coelacanth, with staring blue eyes, lay on the deck of Eric Hunt's schooner. Professor Smith dropped to his knees and began to weep with joy.

Now, with a second coelacanth, he could examine the internal organs of the strange fish. He discovered that the coelacanth had certain valves in its intestines that were found only among a few types of sharks. It had other ancient features as well. But the brain had been ruined by Ahmed Hussein's clubbing, and the body had suffered some damage before it had reached Eric Hunt. So the search for more coelacanths went on.

The next one was caught the following September—a small one, weighing less than ninety pounds. Coelacanth number four was taken in January 1954; the fifth and sixth followed that one by less than a day. It was ten months before the seventh was caught. All these came from the same region, around the Comoro Islands. By now the French, who then owned the Comoros, were interested in getting some coelacanths for their own scientists to study, and a second reward was posted.

On November 12, 1954, the eighth coelacanth was captured. Unlike the first seven, it was a female, which made it a specially important find. Now scientists could compare coelacanths of both sexes. Even more important, number eight was brought in alive.

The fishermen who caught it put it in a swamped boat full of water, and stretched a net over the boat to keep the fish from leaping out. All night long, the happy natives danced in their village while local police guarded the fish. A French icthyologist, Dr. Jacques Millot, arrived in the morning. He was startled to see that a living coelacanth's eyes gave off a strong greenish-yellow glow. But as the sun rose the coelacanth began to show signs of distress.

Professor Millot wrote that it was "seeking to conceal itself in the darkest corners" of the boat. Soon it was "swimming feebly," and then "it had its belly in the air and only the fins and gill covers were making agonized movements." The ninety-pound coelacanth died soon after, and Dr. Millot opened its body to study it.

By now about thirty coelacanths have been captured in the sea off Africa. Most of them are in Paris, but one is in the United States, at New York's American Museum of Natural History. A great deal has been learned about this strange fish since that historic day in 1938. The coelacanth is not nearly so mysterious any more.

This big, tough-looking fish, which grows to a length

of five feet and can weigh as much as 150 pounds, does not seem to be really rare. Native fishermen in the Comoro Islands remember catching—and eating—many large blue fish with shining yellow eyes and odd stalked fins, before scientists began paying good money for them. They even had their own name for the fish: *kombessa.* Probably many coelacanths still remain in the sea.

Though the coelacanth is the most famous living fossil ever discovered, it has not gone through the ages entirely unchanged. Its outer shape has stayed practically the same, but it has shifted its way of life several times. In the Devonian Period most coelacanths lived in the deep sea. About 100 million years later, they were freshwater fish of rivers and lakes. Then they returned to the sea again, now in shallow water not far from shore. Somehow coelacanths were able to hide in the reefs off Africa, adapting to modern life while the other sea creatures of their day died out. An ability to take up life where life was best has kept the coelacanth from extinction. Stalked fins and all, it lingers on millions of years after its time.

Another queer-looking living fossil of the fish world is the lungfish, which has the most unfishlike habit of breathing air when the water in which it lives dries up. Lungfish form a special group among fishes. Their closest relatives are the coelacanths—but the relation is not very close at all.

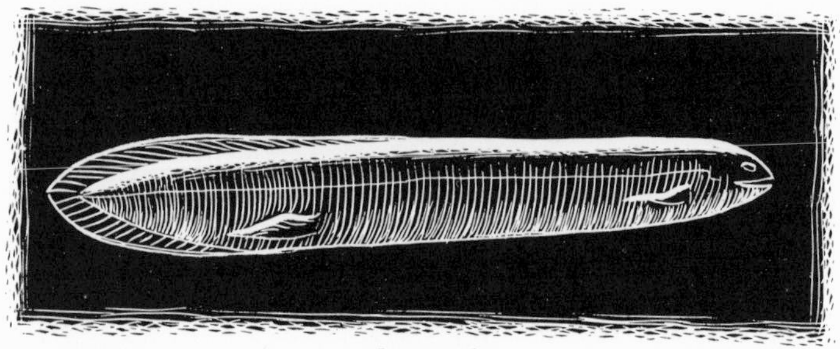

Lungfish

When the first lungfish was discovered in the swamps of the Amazon in 1833, its finder did not know what to make of it. He was Johann Natterer, an Austrian whose main field of interest was ornithology, the study of birds. He spent seventeen years in the jungles of South America, collecting more than twelve thousand specimens of birds. He also happened to collect an eel-like animal that the Indians called *caramuru.* It was a yard long, had four fleshy, paddlelike fins, and crawled about in the mud hunting for snails. Not only did it have gills, it also had a well-developed pair of lungs through which it could breathe.

Natterer had never heard of a fish with lungs. He classed the caramuru as an amphibian, thinking it was some sort of newt or salamander. But when he brought his "newt" back to Austria in 1835, he learned that a similar animal had just been discovered in Africa, and the experts were calling it a fish! This one, too, was some three feet long, lived in river mud, and had two usable lungs besides its gills. It did not look quite as eel-shaped as Natterer's find, and had thicker scales and longer fins. Richard Owen, a great English student of ancient and modern animal life, examined the African animal and said that it was a fish of a very primitive kind. He called it *Protopterus annectens,* "primitive finned creature." Natterer had given his animal the scientific name of *Lepidosiren paradoxus* ("puzzling scaly newt").

Scientists battled over these two creatures for many years. "Fish!" one group cried. "Newt!" roared the others. But finally it was agreed: both *Protopterus* and *Lepidosiren* were fishes—peculiar fishes, but fishes all the same. They were descended from fishes of the Devonian Period, some 300 million years ago. While in water, they breathed through gills, as other fishes did. But each hot season, when the swamps where they lived dried up, the African and South American lungfish simply burrowed into the mud, curled up with their noses toward the surface, and breathed air through their lungs until the water returned. A lungfish caked in mud could be dug out and shipped dry, mud and all, to a far-off part of the world, without suffering any harm.

Though strange and primitive, these two lungfish were not true living fossils. They had evolved greatly from the air-breathing, fleshy-finned fishes of the Devonian, and had turned into very special animals equipped for life in surroundings that were swampy part of the year and dry the rest. There were no fossil fishes known that closely resembled *Protopterus* or *Lepidosiren.*

But a third kind of lungfish turned up after a while—

and this one was a real living fossil by anybody's definition.

In 1869, an Australian farmer who had lived near the Burnett River in the state of Queensland moved to the city of Sydney. He dropped into the Sydney Museum and struck up a conversation with its curator, Gerard Krefft. The farmer asked Krefft why the museum did not display a specimen of the big fish found in the Burnett River.

"Which big fish?" Krefft asked.

"Well, we call it the Burnett Salmon," the farmer replied. "The natives call it something like *barramunda*." He described the fish as being about five feet long, with large greenish scales and four leaf-shaped fins. Its meat was red, like a salmon's, and had an excellent taste.

Krefft was interested. Could the farmer, he asked, help the museum get a Burnett Salmon for its collection? Yes, the farmer said, he could.

"My cousin still lives on our farm," he said. "I'll write to him and have him send a few."

Not many weeks later, a barrel of fish from Queensland arrived at the Sydney Museum. Inside, preserved in a strong salt solution, were several Burnett Salmon. They were as long as a full-grown man, green above and white below, with powerful-looking fleshy fins set on stalks so thick they almost seemed to be little legs. The tail of the Burnett Salmon was not forked like most fishtails; it was just a tapering, pointed fringe.

When he opened the Burnett Salmon's mouth, Krefft got his biggest surprise. It had four large teeth! They were comb-shaped, with many branches, and were made of a hornlike material. Krefft had seen teeth like that before, but not on any modern fish. A certain fossil fish of the dinosaur era had such teeth. It was called *Ceratodus*, meaning "the horn-toothed." Krefft realized that the Burnett Salmon was a living fossil. When he opened one specimen and saw that it had a double breathing system, not only gills but a primitive lung, he knew that this was a relic of a bygone era indeed.

Krefft named the fish for William Forster, the farmer who had told him of it, calling it *Ceratodus forsteri.* The fossil *Ceratodus,* though, was known only from its teeth. Soon, a complete *Ceratodus* fossil was found, and it could be seen that the Burnett Salmon was not quite the same as its ancient ancestor. So it was renamed the "new *Ceratodus,*" *Neoceratodus.* The fossil *Ceratodus* dated from the Mesozoic Era—that is, it had lived about 150 million years ago. Before long, fossils of even older horn-toothed fishes were discovered, pushing the family line back twice as far.

Neoceratodus, the Burnett Salmon or Australian lungfish, is, of course, not a salmon. Nor is it a *barramunda,* for it turned out that Forster was wrong about the native name, and the *barramunda* was another fish entirely. And though it is definitely a lungfish, *Neoceratodus* is only a distant relative of the African and South American kinds.

It has only one lung; they have two. The other lungfishes are long and slender, like eels; *Neoceratodus* is bulky. Its fins are much more paddle-shaped and fleshy. It does not have the ability to curl up in a mudcake and wait for the rainy season; if its gills dry out, it dies. The lung comes into use when *Neoceratodus* finds itself in stale or polluted water that contains little oxygen. Using the water only to keep its gills moist, it gets its air supply by rising to the surface and gulping air into its lung. Even in water that is fresh, this lungfish will surface every hour or two to take a breath of air.

The lungfish give us another clue to the evolutionary story of the first amphibians. They belong to the group of fleshy-finned fishes that found ways to crawl on land and breathe air. But they are evolutionary leftovers, like the coelacanths. The coelacanths never came on land, but remained hidden in the sea. The lungfish hid too—in the mud. Only their more adventurous cousins, the rhidipistians, gave up their fish nature entirely and evolved into land-dwelling creatures.

One more ancient tribe of swimmers has endured the eons with very little change—the sharks. They have 300 million years of history behind them.

The first sharklike creature comes from the Devonian Period, that age of worldwide seas swarming with fish. It is called *Cladoselache* (pronounced clad-o-SEL-a-kee). About three feet long, this graceful animal had parted with the bony armor of the primitive fish known as ostracoderms and placoderms, and depended on speed instead. Its skeleton was made of the soft, flexible material known as cartilage, rather than bone. Its gills and mouth were positioned differently from those of the bony fishes. For these reasons, sharks have always been placed in a special group. Scientists do not consider them true fishes.

Cladoselache became extinct during the Permian Period, about 200 million years ago. By that time, many other types of shark had evolved. Because of their soft skeletons, sharks do not make good fossils, and most of what we know about these early sharks comes from the imprints of their bodies on mud that has turned to rock, not from their actual remains. The only part of a shark that is tough enough to survive and become a fossil is the teeth.

From such fossilized teeth we know that a kind of shark appeared in the Triassic, some 180 million years ago, that had a remarkable dental array. In the front of its mouth were sharp teeth for seizing prey. In the back were flat ones for crushing the shells of mollusks. This type of shark, called a *Hybodont,* was thus able to snare fast-moving fish or to dig up clams and snails from the ocean floor, depending on what was available. One of today's sharks is a direct descendant of the *Hybodonts,* a living fossil little changed from Triassic times. It is the Port Jackson shark (*Heterodontus portjacksoni*) of Australia. About four feet long, with a flattened snout and sharp spines jutting from the front edge of its topmost fins, the Port Jackson shark uses its double set of teeth mostly to feed on mollusks and crustaceans. The Australians often call it the oyster crusher shark. A near relative, the Pacific horned shark, found in the waters off California, is nicknamed the pig shark because of the shape of its head.

Sharks thrived in the dinosaur era. After the dinosaurs were gone, they evolved a giant form of their own, *Carcharodon megalodon,* which lived in the Miocene Period, about 30 million years ago. Just how big *Carcharodon* grew, we can only guess, because nothing but teeth remain. But what teeth! They are six inches high and five and a half inches wide at the base. *Carcharodon's* teeth weigh as much as a pound apiece. The shark was probably sixty to eighty feet long, and some of the biggest ones may have been hundred-footers —as large as the largest known whale. *Carcharodon* is extinct, but it has left a "small" descendant in modern seas, the great white shark. This shark reaches a length of about thirty feet. Its teeth, by way of comparison, are about an inch and a half long.

Though most of the living sharks have evolved in the past few million years, and so cannot be called real

Great White Shark
Port Jackson Shark
Goblin Shark

living fossils, the entire shark group itself is a survivor from antiquity. The bony, or "true" fishes, which appeared later than sharks, have taken command of the seas. There are actually very few species of sharks remaining, compared with the number of bony fishes. But a few shark species, such as the Port Jackson shark mentioned above, have evolved little in millions of years. Another shark that is a living fossil is the goblin shark,

Scapanorhynchus, which was caught off the coast of Japan at the end of the nineteenth century. This little shark, four feet long, had a long, sharp snout and a jaw full of strange, thorny-looking teeth. Fossil sharks 100 million years old with such teeth had been found, but no one had ever seen a living one before. The sea may hold other sharks of ancient type as well, which may turn up at any time on the hooks of startled fishermen.

Not exactly sharks, but distant members of the clan, are the ghost sharks, or *chimaeras.* The chimaera, in Greek mythology, was a fire-breathing beast with a lion's head, the body of a goat, and the tail of a dragon. Our seagoing chimaeras are not as strange as that, but they are distinctly unusual-looking.

They have oversized heads, great staring eyes, and thin bodies that taper away to a long, slender tail. Because their skeletons are made of cartilage, they are grouped with sharks, but the outward resemblance is not very great. Some chimaeras have spikes or hooks growing from their heads, often poisonous. One type, the elephant fish, has a long, drooping, flexible nose. Another that has a remarkable snout is a deep-sea variety called *Harriotta raleighana,* which is about four feet long and lives in the North Atlantic at depths below 3,300 feet. The first one was caught near Virginia, and was named to honor both Thomas Harriott, the sixteenth-century naturalist who was part of the Roanoke colony in 1585, and Sir Walter Raleigh, who organized that colony. (It was Harriott who discovered the American species of the horseshoe crab.)

It might not seem like much of a compliment to have your name attached to as odd a fish as this. It has an enormous pointed nose supported by a stiffening of cartilage, a whiplike tail, and a bulging belly, as well as an ugly spike behind its head. Though fierce-looking, it is actually a timid, harmless fish, as are all the other

Chimaera

chimaeras. They have lasted a long time, according to the fossil records, and they show no sign of becoming extinct soon.

Most of our finny living fossils—the coelacanth, the lungfish from Australia, the chimaeras, and the Port Jackson and goblin sharks—have two characteristics in common. They are all unusual in shape, and they all keep themselves hidden in dark nooks. Perhaps it helps to be funny-looking to survive—and it also helps to know how to stay away from trouble.

Five: THE THREE-EYED ONE, AND OTHERS

ONE DAY IN THE DEVONIAN Period an animal with three toes on each foot walked across a stretch of mud in Pennsylvania and left a clear set of footprints. After 300 million years, those footprints were still there, for the mud had hardened into rock. Those three-toed footprints are the oldest known trace of land animals with backbones.

Those first explorers were amphibians—one step up in the evolutionary scale from fishes. We have already seen how certain fishes were equipped with thick, strong flipperlike fins, and with lungs that allowed them to breathe air. One group of these fishes underwent great changes, their fins turning into feet, their gills disappearing, their lungs becoming more powerful. It took many millions of years for these changes to occur, step by small step. The result was the phylum of amphibians. These animals were born in the water, and had gills when they were young. As it grew older, each amphibian lost its gills and came up on land to live, going back to the water to breed.

Amphibians are very common today. Some, like frogs and toads, live mainly on land when they are adult, and breathe only air. Others—certain kinds of newts and salamanders—keep their gills and spend most of their time in water. None of the amphibians of today can be called a living fossil. They have all appeared quite recently, relatively speaking. They resemble their ancient ancestors only in way of life, not in form.

Those early amphibians had bony coverings on their heads, and in the larger forms were thickly armored. Therefore they are known as *stegocephalians*, a name meaning "roofed heads." Many of them looked somewhat like alligators of today: they had flat, broad heads, outward-staring eyes, and wide mouths. The biggest ones were about fifteen feet long. Most were slow, waddling creatures, but a few were active and swift.

The stegocephalians had one extremely unusual feature—an opening on the top of the skull, behind and midway between the eye sockets. This soft spot in the

Stegocephalian

bony roof probably contained a third eye. For an animal that spent most of its time lying in the mud, a third eye that looked straight up could be very useful.

The next development in evolution produced the reptiles. They looked very much like their ancestors the stegocephalians, at first. But their way of life was quite different. Reptiles were air-breathers from the moment they were born. They laid their eggs on land and did not go through a water-dwelling stage. For many reasons, the reptiles were better able to exist on land than the slow, clumsy amphibians. By the end of the Permian Period, most of the stegocephalians had disappeared, and they died out completely in the next geological period, the Triassic. Reptiles were masters of the world. The amphibians that remained, the ancestors of today's frogs and salamanders, were unimportant creatures.

The great age of reptiles is the Mesozoic Era, divided into three periods: the Triassic, Jurassic, and Cretaceous. During the Mesozoic, reptiles began to evolve in several directions. One group grew enormous in size—the dinosaurs. Another underwent a change in the shape of its ribs, which flattened out and grew together to make a solid armorlike box covering the body—the first turtles and tortoises. A third branch kept the old flat-headed, long-bodied amphibian shape—the ancestors of crocodiles and alligators. A fourth group went back into the water, though continuing to breathe air, and turned into whalelike "sea serpents." Then there were flying reptiles that glided through the air on batlike wings, and small reptiles who became today's lizards, and other reptiles whose legs disappeared as they evolved into snakes.

Most of these reptile classes died out at the end of the Mesozoic. The dinosaurs, the flying reptiles, and the great sea creatures all vanished, leaving the turtles, the lizards, the crocodiles, and little else.

There was one other early kind of reptile that flourished at the time that the amphibians were first giving way to the newcomers. This was the group of *rhynchocephalians,* a name that means "bird-beaked ones." They looked something like lizards, but they had bigger, flatter heads, more like those of crocodiles than of lizards. The rhynchocephalians also kept one feature of their amphibian ancestors—that third eye in the roof of the skull.

The rhynchocephalians were sluggish, stupid animals. They were unable to compete with the faster, smarter reptiles that evolved in the Mesozoic. They hung on through the Triassic Period, but by the Jurassic, some 150 million years ago, they were completely extinct.

Well, *almost* completely.

In 1839, an explorer named Ernst Dieffenbach, visiting New Zealand, was told of a curious large lizard that the Maoris, or native people, called *tuatara, tuatera, nagarara, ruatara,* and several similar-sounding names. "Everything I heard," Dieffenbach wrote later, "seemed to indicate that the lizard was formerly common on all the islands. It lived in caves, and also in sandhills by the shore, and was pursued and killed by the natives for its flesh. As a result of being hunted and also through the introduction of pigs, which ate its young, the animal has become so rare that even many aged inhabitants of the country have never seen it."

New Zealand consists of two large islands, called North Island and South Island, and some smaller ones. Dieffenbach searched everywhere for the tuatara, offering a generous reward for its capture. Only ten days before he was due to leave New Zealand, one was caught and brought to him. A Maori had found it on the little rock-strewn island of Te Karewa, two miles from the coast of North Island. It was still alive, but refused to eat anything Dieffenbach tried to feed it. It died in a few days.

He brought the specimen back to Europe. The tuatara was a plump, dark-green reptile about two feet long that looked like a lizard with an oversized head. Its tail was short and thick, its eyes were huge, and a crest of spines ran down its neck, back, and tail. It was covered with rough, sandy-feeling scales, and its rumpled, wrinkled skin seemed to be, as one writer put it, "too large for the animal inside."

Dieffenbach presented the tuatara to the British Museum. A zoologist named John Edward Gray examined it and gave it the scientific name of *Hatteria punctata*. Looking closely, Gray saw a ring of scales on the crown of the head surrounding a single transparent scale —a kind of peephole. Underneath the transparent scale, Gray discovered, was an organ that looked very much like an eye!

Tuatara

Three-eyed lizards were something brand new to science. But actually this was the second tuatara specimen that had come to the British Museum. Some years before, an unknown collector had captured an animal in New Zealand and sent its skull to London. The same John Edward Gray had written a scientific report on that skull in 1831. He had pointed out certain unusual features of the arrangement of the jaws—and also what he called "a peculiar structure" in the head. Gray had proposed the scientific name *Sphenodon* for this animal. Gradually he came to see that Dieffenbach's tuatara was just a new specimen of *Sphenodon.*

By the rules of scientific naming, the first name given a newly discovered form is supposed to have priority. Gray took back the name of *Hatteria* he had given Dieffenbach's "lizard," and applied the earlier name of *Sphenodon.* Dieffenbach, a German, had published some articles about his find in his own country, and the German zoologists preferred to stick to the *Hatteria* name. So today the three-eyed reptile from New Zealand is called *Sphenodon punctatus* ("pointed wedge-toothed reptile") in English-speaking countries and *Hatteria punctata* elsewhere. Everybody agrees, though, that the animal in question is a tuatara.

And what is a tuatara?

Not a lizard, though it looks like one. The tuatara is the last of the rhynchocephalians, the beak-headed, three-eyed reptiles that lived before the dinosaurs. Unlike all other living reptiles, it has teeth that grow right out of its jawbone; thick, unusual ribs; and vertebrae with hollow sides. It also has that third eye.

The extra eye does not really see. It is smaller than the other two, and is covered by the transparent scale that almost entirely hides it. But there is a nerve leading from the eye to the tuatara's brain. Probably the eye can register changes in light and dark, if nothing more. In the millions of years since the other rhynchocephalians died out, the tuatara's third eye has lost most of its function—though not all.

One other living animal has at least the remnant of a third eye. It is a large black lizard that lives on the Galapagos Islands off South America. However, that creature's third eye is less well developed than tuatara's, and is not as sensitive to light and dark. In almost all living reptiles it is possible to detect the place where the third eye used to be; there is often a tiny opening in the skull, and a small round growth that is the evolutionary descendant of the extra eye, hidden beneath the skin. Even human beings still show traces of the time when animals had three eyes. Attached to the top of the human brain is a tiny, cone-shaped organ known as the *pineal gland.* No one knows what purpose it serves. It is the lingering survivor of the third eye, now covered by the skull.

Tuataralike reptiles once were found in many parts of the world. A fossil rhynchocephalian called *Homeosaurus* has been unearthed in England and Bavaria; it lived 145 million years ago, and from its skeleton it seems to have looked almost exactly like tuatara. The three-eyed ones spread down through Asia into Malaya. In the Jurassic, land bridges connected many of the islands of the Pacific. Crossing on these bridges, the tuatara got from Malaya to what is now the island of New Guinea, from there to New Caledonia, and then to New Zealand's North Island. Some time later, the land bridges sank. New Zealand was separated from the rest of the world, and the tuatara remained undisturbed in its remote island home.

Today New Zealand is the only place in the world where it can be found, and it is rare even there. It lives only on a few small islands. On the two main islands, tuatara was exterminated long ago by the pigs and dogs brought to New Zealand by the white settlers who came there late in the eighteenth century. New Zealand does not have any large native animals, and the tuatara had no enemies before the white man imported some.

It is against the law in New Zealand to kill a tuatara or even to keep one as a pet. You have to get a government permit simply to visit one of the islands where they live. About half a dozen live ones have been allowed to go overseas to foreign zoos—the San Diego Zoo in California was one of the lucky ones—and a few museums in the United States, such as the American Museum of Natural History in New York, have stuffed ones on display.

The tuatara needs to be protected in this way because it is one of the sleepiest, most slow-moving animals in the world. It can move quickly when it has to, but it does not do so often; its only other means of defense is to snap with its powerful jaws. The bite of the tuatara is said to be a painful one, and once its jaws are closed it is slow to let go.

Generally, it sleeps. It hardly even bothers to breathe. One scientist watched a tuatara for an hour without seeing it draw a breath. At best, when excited, it breathes about once every seven seconds. When hunting its food —beetles, centipedes, snails, and flies, caught at night— it pounces swiftly, but then it sinks back into dreaminess again. It chews slowly, with a long pause between each bite. Sometimes it falls asleep while still eating, a piece of food gripped tightly in its mouth.

The tuatara is just as lazy about its housekeeping. It lives with a bird called the petrel, which digs a burrow in the ground as its nest. After a petrel has made its tunnel, a tuatara will move in. The bird and the reptile seem to get along well with each other. More accurately, they ignore each other—even when a brood of squawking petrel chicks disturbs the tuatara's sleep. The reptile never goes near the young petrels. Perhaps its dim brain can grasp the fact that it would finish second best in a contest with an angry, sharp-clawed mother bird.

The tuatara is slow to come into the world, and slow to leave it. The leathery-shelled eggs take thirteen months to hatch, which is an extremely long time. The eggs of a giant tortoise hatch in only eight months, for example. How long the tuatara lives is unknown, because the animal is difficult to study, and often outlives its studiers. The Maoris claim that a captive tuatara lived in a pit on one of the New Zealand islands for almost three hundred years. New Zealand zoos have kept tuataras alive more than fifty years. It is possible that its average lifespan is several centuries.

The first European explorer to land on New Zealand's shores was Captain James Cook. He came there in 1769. Tucked away in burrows, safely out of sight, were the sleepy survivors of the beak-headed reptiles, the rhynchocephalians, living fossils unchanged over 150 million years. It is strange to think that some of the tuataras who were alive when Captain Cook landed may still be there today—a little drowsier, but as healthy as ever.

The rest of today's reptiles are not so ancient. Most of them, in fact, evolved during the last few million years. Others can be regarded as living fossils of a sort, though they have changed with the passing of time.

Usually the change is one of size. Crocodiles and alligators have not altered much since the Cretaceous—except to get smaller. Today's crocodiles, fifteen or twenty feet long, are not precisely dainty, but they hardly compare with their mighty ancestors. The biggest of all the ancient crocodiles was *Phobosuchus,* who grew to a length of fifty or sixty feet. (And lived in Texas, of course.)

Turtles and tortoises, also, have come down in size. The bulky Galapagos tortoises are no match for such extinct monsters as *Colossochelys atlas,* an Indian tortoise of a million years ago. That one reached a length of twelve feet. A *small* specimen at the American Museum of Natural History measures seven feet four inches long over the curve of the carapace or upper shell, and is five feet wide. It weighed over a ton when alive.

Another jumbo was the sea turtle *Archelon,* which lived in Nebraska during the Cretaceous, when an inland sea covered central North America. *Archelon* was eleven

Archelon

Galapagos Tortoise

feet long, with a flipper-spread of a dozen feet. The biggest sea turtles of our time reach lengths of eight or nine feet, but they are quite different in appearance from *Archelon*, having much less body armor.

The closest thing to a living fossil in the turtle-tortoise family is the Galapagos tortoise, sometimes called a turtle. (Which it is depends on where you live. In England, *turtles* are sea creatures with paddle-shaped flippers, and the rest are *tortoises.* In the United States, most land-dwellers are called *tortoises* and most water-dwellers are considered *turtles.* But the common box "turtle" lives on land, while "tortoise shell" for eyeglass frames comes from sea-dwellers. And the Galapagos giants are called tortoises by some writers and turtles by others, though they are land animals.)

The first European to see giant land tortoises was probably an English skipper named John Jourdain, who found them on the Seychelles Islands in the Indian Ocean. One of his men wrote that they were "of so huge a bigness which men will think incredible," and said they were equipped "with five claws like a bear."

About a hundred years afterward, the pirate captain William Dampier found similar animals on the Galapagos Islands, which lie in the Pacific off the coast of Ecuador. "They are extraordinarily large and fat," Dampier wrote, and so many could be found that they would provide food for five or six hundred men. Later, other islands in the Indian Ocean north of Madagascar also proved to have colonies of giant land tortoises. The

Indian Ocean tortoises are related to the Galapagos ones. Some weigh as much as six hundred pounds and live for centuries. No one has been able to explain why these giants should be found only on these widely separated island groups.

The Galapagos Islands, just below the equator and six hundred miles west of the South American coast, are hot and dry. Most of their plants are cacti and other thorny desert types. The islands were formed by the action of volcanoes, and their beaches are covered by twisted masses of lava.

Probably the most important visit to the Galapagos Islands took place on September 15, 1835, when H.M.S. *Beagle* dropped anchor there. That was the research ship that was carrying Charles Darwin on his five-year voyage around the world.

He found a host of animals unlike those known elsewhere. There was a seagoing lizard, which swam out to nibble seaweed—the only lizard in the world with such habits. There were the giant tortoises. There were unusual birds. Here, Darwin saw, were islands cut off from the rest of the world by hundreds of miles of ocean. Somehow, animals had reached the islands. Then, living in complete isolation, they had gone through changes that set them apart from mainland animals. Much of Darwin's evolution theory, published twenty-four years later, stemmed from ideas that came to him while studying the animals and plants of the Galapagos Islands.

Naturally, he was fascinated by the giant tortoises. They seemed to him like beings from the dawn of time—though we know today that they are just latecomers compared with a real living fossil like the tuatara. Darwin went scrambling through thorny thickets and rough lava beds to reach the tortoises, with the sun "glowing hot" overhead. At last, the great scientist came face to face with the ancient beasts. The meeting between man and reptile was not very successful. This is how Darwin describes the encounter:

"As I was walking along I met two large tortoises, each of which must have weighed at least two hundred pounds: one was eating a piece of cactus, and as I approached, it stared at me and slowly stalked away; the other gave a deep hiss, and drew in its head."

Obviously the tortoises failed to realize they were making history.

Six: BIRDS THAT DON'T FLY

New Zealand, the home of the tuatara, is a lonely place, geographically speaking. For the past 100 million years, a thousand miles of ocean has separated New Zealand from its nearest neighbor, Australia. Before that, as we have seen, land bridges tied New Zealand and some other Pacific island regions to Southeast Asia. When the bridges sank, during the Cretaceous, New Zealand was cut off, and the unusual animals it contained were left to develop undisturbed.

Man was late to get there. The Polynesian seafarers known as Maoris reached New Zealand less than a thousand years ago. They brought dogs and rats, which began to attack the harmless birds and reptiles that made up most of New Zealand's animal population. In 1642, the Dutch explorer Abel Tasman arrived, but looked and left without coming ashore. Captain Cook was next, in 1769, and soon afterward European settlers were landing.

In 1812, the English ship *Providence* visited New Zealand. Its captain collected some specimens of New Zealand wildlife and brought them back to London. Among them was the skin of a bird that puzzled the British Museum's experts no end.

The bird was about the size of a hen. It had no sign of wings or a tail. It seemed to be covered with a shaggy coat of hair, rather than feathers. Its four-toed feet were huge, and so was its beak, which had nostrils placed right at the tip. It looked more like a hobgoblin than a bird.

One of the scientists gave it a Latin name: *Apteryx australis,* "southern bird without wings." Another thought it might be related to the penguins. A third man suggested it was a dwarf ostrich. A fourth grouped it with the extinct bird called the dodo, which also was unable to fly. A German professor said it was part of the family of long-billed birds known as snipes, and gave it the name of *Schnepfenstrauss*, "snipe-ostrich."

In time the truth became clear. The hairy, long-billed

bird from New Zealand belonged in a special group of birds called *Ratites*, which had stopped flying 100 million years ago, or possibly never did fly at all. It was not a close relative of the snipe (which flies quite well) or the dodo (which once could fly before it got too heavy) or the penguin (which does its "flying" under water). But the wingless furry bird—which the Maoris called the *kiwi*—was in fact linked to the ostrich.

The ostrich and the kiwi are just two of the Ratites. Others include the emu of Australia, the rhea of South America, and the cassowary of the Pacific islands. There are also some extinct giant forms: the *moa* of New Zealand, which stood nearly twelve feet high, and the *Aepyornis* of Madagascar, the biggest bird that ever lived, a ten-footer that laid eggs thirteen inches across.

All these birds have special features setting them apart from other birds. They are unable to fly; some lack wings altogether, others have very weak ones. They do not have the strong breastbones that support the powerful wing muscles of flying birds. Their feathers are stringy, looking more like fur or hair. They lay huge eggs. And their legs are very strong—the kick of an ostrich, for instance, can kill a man.

These flightless birds are living fossils that tell us a great deal about evolution. We do not know, however, whether they have been changed by time. Very little fossil information is available about them. Even the extinct forms, the moa and the *Aepyornis*, died out only a few centuries ago. What the Ratites looked like 20 million years ago is still unknown, and will be until fossil remains are discovered. How can we call them living fossils, then, if we do not have the fossils of their ancestors?

We think they are because they look much more primitive than the flying birds. They *seem* ancient. They appear to go back to the time when the first birds were evolving.

That was in the Jurassic, when dinosaurs walked the earth. The oldest known fossil bird is called *Archaeopteryx*, a name that means "ancient bird." It was about the size of a pigeon, with a long lizardlike tail fringed with feathers. Its wings developed from the fingers and lower arms of its forelimbs, and still kept four bony claws along the upper edge. *Archaeopteryx* also had a full set of sharp teeth, unlike all modern birds. It looked like something halfway between lizard and bird, which is what it was. Scales had become feathers. The feathers kept the *Archaeopteryx* warm. When birds grew feathers, they were able to evolve into warm-blooded creatures—that is, animals whose body temperature stayed pretty much the same all the time. Reptiles, amphibians, and fish are all cold-blooded, and their temperature changes to match that of their surroundings. Warm-blooded animals are suited for a more active life than cold-blooded ones, and are more intelligent, so this was an upward step in evolution.

Archaeopteryx was able to fly, and so was *Ichthyornis*, another early toothed bird. This Cretaceous bird was a

Kiwi

Archaeopteryx

kind of primitive sea gull. But *Hesperornis,* a six-foot-long Cretaceous bird, was a swimmer and diver that lacked wings entirely, and has sometimes been called the "toothed swimming ostrich." It shows that wingless birds existed more than 80 million years ago.

Perhaps some Jurassic or Cretaceous family of small dinosaurs evolved into the ancestors of the kiwi and the ostrich. Many dinosaurs walked on their hind legs and were only a few feet tall; one of them, *Struthiomimus,* looked so much like a scaly ostrich that its name means "the ostrich mimic." Unfortunately, we lack the fossil evidence that could show that such dinosaurs sprouted feathers, became warm-blooded, and turned into flightless birds. The oldest ostrich fossils we have discovered so far are only about a million years old, except for one ostrichlike bird that may be twenty times as ancient.

So it is only a guess—but scientists think it is a good one—that the flightless two-legged birds are members of an ancient line of evolution, separate from the main stock of flying birds. In any case they are strange and curious animals, which look as though they *ought* to be living fossils.

The kiwi is the strangest of all. Actually, we should speak of the kiwis, for there are three species, the common kiwi, the little spotted kiwi, and the great spotted kiwi. Once there was a giant kiwi, the size of a turkey, but it is now extinct.

All the species of kiwi have the same habits. They are forest birds that sleep by day; sunlight hurts their eyes, and if they are awakened in daytime they look indignant and upset, sometimes yawning an immense yawn to show annoyance. At twilight they emerge, scurrying around looking for the worms and insects that they eat. The kiwi is the only living bird that has a sense of smell —if other birds ever had it, they lost it millions of years ago—and it can be heard making loud sniffing noises as it pokes its bill along the ground. When it comes on a morsel of food, it pounces quickly, driving its long bill into the ground to pull up a worm or a bug. It has sharp, powerful claws, which it uses to defend itself.

The kiwi is a comical-looking creature to begin with, and its occasional habit of sleeping in a "three-legged" position, resting the tip of its bill on the ground, makes it seem even more amusing. New Zealanders love the kiwi; it can be seen on their coins and stamps, and it is protected by strict laws. Once, a kiwi was caught by accident in a rat trap, and its ankle was broken. New Zealand bird-lovers designed an artificial leg for it, taught it how to walk with it, and turned the kiwi loose! Though treated so carefully, the kiwi is a rare bird, and not many New Zealanders have ever seen it in the wild. It is said to be an unforgettable sight when a kiwi comes through the woods, stooped over with its bill near the ground, sniffing loudly, looking more like a hedgehog than like a bird.

Perhaps the most unbelievable thing about the kiwi is the size of its eggs. Though no bigger than a hen, a kiwi lays eggs as big as an ostrich's. Kiwi eggs as large as 5 by 2¾ inches have been laid—weighing a third as much as the bird that laid them!

From Australia, a land of many strange creatures, comes the emu—another flightless bird, though it has wings. It is a gray-brown in color, with black tips on the feathers. Looking something like a smaller version of the ostrich, the emu has hairlike feathers on its long neck. The female lays seven to thirteen big eggs at a time.

Emu

Australia, too, is the home of the cassowary, found also on the Pacific islands north of Australia. Closely related to the emu, the cassowary is much more colorful, with blue-black plumage and bright blue and red wattles on its neck. A striking-looking horny helmet grows on the head.

South America's contribution to the Ratites is the rhea, or South American ostrich. A handsome bird more than five feet tall, it lives in Argentina, Brazil, and high in the Andes. Darwin saw a rhea on his *Beagle* voyage, and wrote that it "presented a very noble appearance." One of the three species of rhea is named for him: *Rhea darwini.* Rheas have an odd nesting habit; several rhea hens will lay their eggs in the same nest, so that one nest might contain more than thirty eggs. Darwin found four nests close together with a total of ninety-three eggs in them. One nest had twenty-seven eggs, each as big as eleven eggs of the sort sold in grocery stores, so that Darwin and his friends made an enormous 297-egg

Cassowary

omelet out of them. It is the male rhea that sits on the eggs and takes care of the young. Only a brave man goes near a rhea nest while the male is on it. The great bird defends its eggs and chicks fiercely, charging any enemy with wings spread wide, neck outstretched, and powerful legs ready to lash out in a terrible kick.

The best-known of this group of birds is the African ostrich, which is also the biggest. Some ostriches are eight feet tall and weigh more than three hundred pounds. They are swift runners and good fighters. Like the rhea, the ostrich shares its nest. The ostrich resembles the rhea in so many ways (it is larger, and has two toes instead of three, but those are the chief differences) that scientists have had trouble explaining how such similar flightless birds got from one continent to

Ostrich *Rhea*

another. One theory is that long ago Africa and South America were much closer than they are now, or that land bridges connected them. The land bridge idea was very popular in the nineteenth century, leading Charles Darwin to say in annoyance that one scientist invented land bridges "as easily as a cook makes pancakes." Today the authorities are not so sure how the animals spread to the different parts of the world.

Another bird that does not fly, and that can be called a living fossil, is that solemn, dignified inhabitant of the far south, the penguin. Fossil penguins found in Antarctica have been given an age of 50 million years.

Eighteen species of penguin are known today. Only two of these live in the Antarctic—the emperor penguin and the Adélie. Others inhabit the chilly islands just outside the Antarctic Circle, but there are penguins native to Australia and New Zealand, the west coast of South America, South Africa, and even the Galapagos Islands, just south of the equator. The biggest of these, the emperor, reaches a size of about three and a half feet, a weight of ninety pounds. But two extinct penguins of 25 million years ago were five feet tall and weighed from two to three hundred pounds, so evolution has made the penguin smaller with time.

About twenty-five kinds of fossil penguins are known. The first was discovered in 1859, and since then they have been unearthed throughout the Southern Hemisphere. Although none of these fossil penguins is exactly like any of the living types, the differences are not great. We do not know how the penguin evolved, because we are lacking a series of changing fossil types. For the horse, to take a good example, we have a complete range from the tiny *Eohippus*, with its four toes, through the small three-toed and one-toed horses to the horse of today. But the earliest penguin fossils are already fully evolved penguins.

One guess is that originally the penguins could fly, and were similar to such sea birds as the pelican, the petrel, and the albatross. Living in the cold regions of the Antarctic, the penguins found few flying insects to eat, but plenty of fish in the water. It was more useful to be able to swim than to fly, and gradually the penguins' wings turned into flippers, making them fast-moving creatures in the water, but condemning them to waddle along clumsily on land.

Though all penguins today have the same general body plan, there are wide differences betwen the species. Some are able to resist the sixty-below-zero cold of a winter at the South Pole; others are adapted for life on the tropical Galapagos. When on land, some penguins walk, others jump; some are able to climb the faces of steep cliffs, others have learned how to catapult themselves out of water with a sudden quick flip of their wings and legs. They are of different sizes and different colors, and each species has its own nesting and feeding habits. But nobody who sees a penguin of any sort is likely to mistake it for some other kind of bird.

The first Europeans who saw penguins *did* manage to confuse them with other birds, though—and thereby hangs the story of how the penguin got its name.

Once a large flightless bird called the giant auk lived in the cold Arctic regions. It had strong wings adapted for swimming, a big beak, and a dark brown head with white patches around the eyes. The fishermen from Brittany who hunted the giant auk called it by the ancient Welsh name *pen-gwyn*, "white head." That reminded scholars of the Latin word *pinguis*, meaning "fat." Since the giant auk was plump and tasty, they called it *pinguin*, "fat bird," and this blended with the *pen-gwyn* of the fishermen to become *penguin.*

The giant auk was so useful—its eggs made good food, its oily flesh was handy for lamp fuel—that the

Emperor Penguin *Adélie Penguin*

fishermen hunted it into extinction. Millions of giant auks lived in Newfoundland and Labrador when the first European explorers got there at the end of the fifteenth century. By 1830, there were less than a hundred left, living on a single island near Iceland, and in a few more years these "penguins" of the Arctic were extinct.

There is no relation at all between giant auks and the penguins of the south. But when mariners began to venture below the equator they discovered curious birds that they called "southern penguins," because they seemed to resemble the giant auks. So the name was transferred, and the "fat birds" or "white heads" of the Arctic gave their name to the dignified dinner-jacketed birds of the Southern Hemisphere.

The first Europeans to see the southern penguins were the men who sailed around the world with Magellan. In 1520, they found huge flocks of "strange geese" on the coast of Patagonia, near the tip of South America. Fifty-eight years later, Sir Francis Drake traveled the same route. A member of his expedition wrote that "we found great store of fowl which could not fly, of the bigness of geese." He said they killed three thousand in a single day to use as food.

Before long these "strange geese" were being called penguins. When that great voyager Captain Cook became the first to approach Antarctica, in 1773, he found the ice-covered islands of the far south thronging with the birds. Some had red eyes and bright yellow crests;

some had black chin straps and dark wings; some had brilliant orange bibs. The discovery of more species of penguins followed. Some, like the Galapagos penguin, remained unknown until late in the nineteenth century.

Long before there were men or even apes, penguins strutted upright over the southern ice, and swam briskly through the chilly waters. For 50 million years they have not changed their basic pattern. Someday we may know their early evolutionary history. Its secrets probably lie buried under tons of Antarctic ice. What we do know is that long ago the penguin reached a form perfectly suited to life in the coldest part of the world—and stuck to it.

The last of our living fossils among the birds is one that can fly, after a fashion, when it wants to. But it very rarely wants to. It would much rather swim. When on land, it moves through treetops using its feet and wings. Its young ones have their own special way of climbing from branch to branch: they use the claws that sprout from their wings, claws that become useless when the bird gets older.

No bird alive today shows more clearly that birds are descended from lizards. If you can imagine a lizard with feathers and wings, you can picture the *hoatzin* of South America.

The natives call it the stinkbird. If the wind is right, a flock of hoatzins can be smelled at a great distance. The unusual and powerful odor has been known to remain even after a stuffed hoatzin has been on display in a museum for several years. The scent reminds some people of the smell of turtles or crocodiles.

The hoatzin is about the size of a large pigeon. It is yellowish in color, with an olive-green back and a dull red belly. A high comblike crest of yellow feathers sprouts from its head. It lives in the swampy jungles of British Guiana and the Amazon Valley, always staying close to water. In British Guiana the hoatzin nests in two plants called *mucka-mucka* and *bunduri pimpler*, which line the banks of streams. The bird is an excellent swimmer, and spends most of its time in the water. It makes its nests in low branches a few feet above the surface of the water. When not swimming, the hoatzin stays close to home, clambering around in nearby trees.

Even a short flight is a big effort. The hoatzin launches itself into space, making a weird froglike croaking sound, and flutters awkwardly to the nearest perch. If it has to travel as much as fifty feet, it often makes a forced landing on the ground midway through the trip, to rest. Sometimes, after flying from one tree to the next, the hoatzin gets so weary that it digs its toes into a branch and topples over, hanging upside down while it recovers. Usually, instead of flying at all, the bird scrambles through the branches, flapping its wings and using its claws to pull itself along. This gives the wing feathers and tail feathers a frayed, bedraggled look.

Adult hoatzins are odd birds, but the young ones are fantastic. When they hatch they are long-necked and ugly, without any feathers at all. Their wings have sharp curved claws on the front edges, three to each wing. Looking strangely like the *Archaeopteryx,* that lizard-bird of the Jurassic, the baby hoatzins climb slowly through the trees, nibbling tender leaves, using their wing-claws almost like fingers. In the water, the chicks seem like some sort of lizard as they flash rapidly by. When they get older, the feathers sprout. In an adult hoatzin the wing-claws are completely hidden by feathers and can no longer be used for climbing.

The hoatzin has few enemies, because its unpleasant smell and taste tend to discourage animals and men from eating it. The snakes and crocodiles that live in the streams below the hoatzin nests are not so fussy about their diet, and make a quick mouthful of any hoatzin

Hoatzin

that comes within reach. When an intruder comes near the nest, hoatzins young and old escape the same way—by jumping out and diving headfirst into the water. Even a fledgling hoatzin will make the jump fearlessly, dropping as much as twelve feet and immediately swimming to shore. Sometimes the gaping mouth of a crocodile waits right under a hoatzin nest, but that does not stop these not-too-bright birds from diving anyway.

No other bird is closely related to the hoatzin. With its claw-adorned fingers, its froglike cry, its turtlelike smell, its skill in swimming, and its clumsiness as a flier, it seems to stand midway between reptiles and birds. It is a creature stranded in time, the relic of a forgotten world.

Seven: WOMBATS, WALLABIES, AND BANDICOOTS

EARLY IN THE SEVENTEENTH century, bold seamen of the Dutch East India Company sailed westward to look for the spice-rich islands of the Pacific. They discovered a large new land which they patriotically called New Holland. In 1629, a Dutch captain named Francis Pelsart was shipwrecked there, and sighted a mysterious animal, as big as a man, with a long tail and a head like a deer's. It stood on its hind legs, and could hop like a frog. Strangest of all, Pelsart said, it carried its young in a pouch on the belly!

Europeans found it hard to believe in Pelsart's beast. Nor were they convinced when the pirate William Dampier visited the west coast of New Holland in 1699 and reported "a sort of raccoon" with "very short forelegs," which got about by jumping. Not until Captain Cook reached New Holland in 1770 did people begin to accept the fact that this huge continent-sized island was full of unlikely animals.

Cook sent three of his crewmen inland to shoot pigeons for food, on June 23, 1770. They came back talking of a slender, fast-moving animal of a curious shape. The next day Cook himself saw one. He wrote, "I should have taken it for a wild dog, but for its walking or running in which it jumped like a hare or a deer." Two weeks later, one of his officers killed one, and Cook noted in his journal, "It bears no sort of resemblance to any European animal I ever saw."

He asked the natives what the jumping animal was called. "*Kangaroo,*" they answered. Perhaps they were just telling Cook that they didn't understand his question. The word *kangaroo* is not known to exist in any of the native languages of New Holland, which we call Australia today. However, Cook accepted *kangaroo* as the animal's name, and the name stuck.

He collected some kangaroos to be studied in London, and captured two other Australian animals as well, which lived in trees and were covered with long wool. Cook did not notice that all three of these animals had pouches for carrying the young. That was observed later. Eventually more than two hundred different kinds of mammals were discovered in Australia. None of them was like any animal found elsewhere. *All* of them raised their young in pouches. Scientists realized that Australia was an enormous open-air museum inhabited entirely by living fossils—a whole continent full of them.

Animals with pouches are called *marsupials*, from the Latin word *marsupium*, "pouch." The marsupials were the first mammals to evolve. These small, hairy animals began to develop late in the era of dinosaurs. They were warm-blooded, and lived on insects, nuts, seeds, and—probably—the eggs of dinosaurs. Fast-moving and alert, they learned how to keep out of the way of the big reptiles that lumbered about.

Kangaroo

Some of these early mammals laid eggs like reptiles. But most of them brought their young ones into the world already hatched. (A few reptiles bore their young alive also. They were probably the ancestors of the mammals.) When a reptile cracked its egg and emerged into the world, it was on its own and got no help from its parents. It had to find food for itself, right away, or it would perish. Mammals had an easier time. When they were born, blind and practically helpless, they crawled into a pouch on their mother's belly. The pouch contained nipples that gave milk. There they remained, nourished by their mother's milk, until they were old enough to look after themselves.

Toward the end of the Cretaceous Period, the dinosaurs began to disappear. They had ruled the world for more than 140 million years. The last of the big reptiles died about 70 million years ago. Now the world belonged to the mammals. They spread to every continent. Many new forms appeared—the early ancestors of the horse, the cat, the dog, the hippopotamus, and all the rest of today's mammals. The first apelike creatures evolved too, 30 or 40 million years ago.

But the marsupial mammals met competition. A new kind of mammal developed, equipped with an organ called a *placenta*. The placenta is a kind of wrapper that surrounds an unborn mammal in its mother's womb. The baby is connected to the placenta by the *umbilical cord*. Food and blood travel through the placenta and the umbilical cord from mother to child. The young of placental mammals remain in the womb much longer than those of marsupials. When they finally are born, they are much stronger and more active than newborn marsupials, though they still need their mother's care for a while.

The placental mammals thrived at the expense of the more primitive marsupials. Though we are not sure exactly why, marsupials became extinct almost everywhere in the world. They survived on a large scale only in Australia.

Australia, many millions of years ago, was connected to Asia by a series of land bridges. That was how mammals first got to Australia. Very early in the age of mammals, however, the bridges sank. Australia was cut off. The placental mammals that later took possession of the rest of the world had no way of getting there. For some reason, placental mammals never evolved in Australia, leaving the marsupials in charge.

The first placental mammal to reach Australia was man. He got there a few hundred thousand years ago, at the very earliest. That is just a moment ago, compared with the 80-million-year history of mammals. He brought another placental animal with him, the dog. Later, cats and foxes came to Australia. Whenever placental mammals and marsupials try to occupy the same place, the marsupials always lose. So one marsupial after another became extinct in Australia. By the time Europeans arrived on the Australian scene, many marsupial species had vanished forever.

At the end of the eighteenth century the English began to colonize Australia. Only convicts were sent there at first, but within a few years free men were arriving to try their luck as settlers. They built towns along the coasts. Slowly, explorers began to push inland into the jungles and deserts of the unknown continent. Marsupials galore were discovered, trapped, and sent back to Europe for study.

Pouched animals were not new to zoologists. They already knew about the opossum that lived in America. Vincent Pinzon, who sailed with Columbus, brought an opossum to Spain in 1500 to show to King Ferdinand and Queen Isabella. They were fascinated by it, even exploring the inside of its pouch with their royal fingers. But now hundreds of marsupials were being discovered all at once!

As the picture of Australian animal life became clearer, zoologists realized that the marsupials had evolved into many of the same forms as the placental mammals of other continents. Kangaroos were the marsupial version of deer and antelope. There were marsupial mice, marsupial bears, marsupial rats, marsupial squirrels, marsupial moles, marsupial rabbits, marsupial wolves, and many others. A kind of marsupial lion had once existed, but was now extinct, as was a marsupial rhinoceros.

Of course, these animals did not resemble their placental doubles too closely. The marsupial "cat," for instance, would never be mistaken for one of our tabbies. But it was interesting that every slot in nature had been filled by a marsupial that played the same part as a placental animal did elsewhere. From big flesh-eaters down to tiny nut-eaters, the range of life forms was the same. (With one major exception: there were no marsupial apes—nor were there any marsupial men!)

The marsupial wonderland of Australia contains more animals than we could possibly discuss in this book. It is important to realize, by the way, that although all of the native animals of Australia are living fossils in one sense, most of them are not in another. That is, since they are marsupials they represent an ancient kind of mammal with millions of years of ancestry. But taken one by one the Australian marsupials are recent forms. Evolution has continued in Australia as in the rest of the world, and its isolated population of marsupials shows the changes of time.

The kangaroo was the first to be discovered. The explorers found that kangaroos come in all sizes and a variety of shapes. They range from the big red kangaroo of the inland plains and the great gray kangaroo of the forests, which reach lengths of nine feet from snout to tail-tip, down to little ones like the rat kangaroos, which are smaller than rabbits. Today's Australian settlers have kept many of the native names, such as that of the wallaroo, a medium-sized jumper, and the wallaby, a smaller 'roo.

It is believed that the first marsupials lived in trees, and—improbable as it sounds—some kangaroos have gone back there. These are the tree kangaroos, with slim tails that they use for balancing, and big hind feet armed with hooked claws. Clumsy on the ground, they leap smoothly from branch to branch.

Another tree-dweller is the Australian opossum, now usually called just "possum" to keep it from being confused with the American kind, to which it is not related. Some of these possums are gliding possums that swoop gracefully from tree to tree, as flying squirrels do in North America. Others are roly-poly waddlers.

The banded anteater, which the natives call the *numbat*, is a rat-sized marsupial that has more teeth than any other living mammal—more than fifty of them. Numbats are similar to fossil marsupial types more than 60 million years old. Furry, rust-red animals with tongues four inches long, they live only in one part of Western Australia, and make termites their favorite meal. A numbat eats as many as twenty thousand termites a day.

About 1800, a small furry marsupial was found in the towering eucalyptus trees of Australia's Blue Mountains. It looked exactly like a teddy bear—though teddy bears had not yet been invented. The natives called it *kullawine*, which became *koala* to the settlers. They also spoke of it as the "gum-tree monkey" and the "Australian bear." The gentle, friendly koala clings to the branches with monkeylike paws that have two thumbs, and eats a pound or two of eucalyptus leaves a day. Because the koala will eat only a certain type of leaf, its existence is threatened. As the cities of Australia

Australian Opossum

Kangaroo Rat *Numbat*

grow, more and more eucalyptus trees are chopped down. Unable to adapt to a different kind of food, the koala is losing ground as the trees disappear.

Australians are fond of this lovable-looking marsupial, and they have set aside special sanctuaries for the koala. But they have not always been kind to it in the past. At the beginning of this century millions of koalas inhabited Australia, but they were killed in great numbers for their valuable fur. In 1924 alone, 2 million koala skins were sold by Australia. Today koalas are no longer hunted, but only a few thousand still exist. It is probably too late to save them from extinction.

Also vanishing is the *wombat*, a fat, heavy creature that looks like a small grizzly bear. Sailors aboard a British ship shot a wombat in 1789; the ship was wrecked and washed up on an island near Australia, and the governor found the animal and sent its skin to London. A naturalist there called it a "bear-like marsupial rat," a good description. The wombat lives in deep burrows, and feeds on grass and leaves. Though strong enough to crush a dog that tries to invade its burrow, the wombat is usually gentle, and some Australians keep them as pets. The wombat is the bulkiest of today's marsupials; some of its ancestors were as big as hippopotamuses. (The smallest marsupial is the *pla-nigale,* which weighs only a fifth of an ounce. It eats insects larger than itself.)

The list of Australian marsupials goes on and on. There is the *cuscus,* for instance, a plump tree-dwelling possum that spends its days sleeping with its tail neatly rolled into a ring. Brightly colored and slow-moving, the cuscus is covered with thick woolly fur. Less cuddly-looking is the Tasmanian devil, a doglike marsupial with a big head and a fierce-looking mouth. It makes a loud, frightening sound, a mixture of a whine and a snarl, that leads some people to call it the Australian hyena. Its bigger cousin, the *thylacine,* or Tasmanian wolf, is almost extinct. This ferocious wolflike marsu-pial was an enemy to the early settlers, who killed it in great numbers. Few real wolves could look as men-acing, for the thylacine's jaws could open to a great

Tasmanian Devil

Wombat

width—"almost to the ears," one observer said. No one has seen this animal alive in many years, but its footprints have been spotted in the jungles of Tasmania, and perhaps a few continue to survive.

The forests of Australia still hold such oddities as the *bandicoot*, a long-nosed animal the size of a rat, and the *quoll*, a small brown beast with white spots that has some of the grace of a cat. Another catlike marsupial is the *dasyure*, which has been nearly wiped out by farmers trying to protect their poultry from this fast-moving flesh-eater.

Wallabies, wombats, bandicoots, and the rest of Australia's novel menagerie may not be living fossils much longer. The spread of civilization in Australia is pushing them toward the vanishing point. Such placental

Dasyure

Bandicoot

American Opossum

mammals as dogs, cats, mice, rats, and rabbits have been introduced, and they are making life difficult for the hard-pressed marsupials. Though the Australians are trying to protect their open-air museum of animals, too much harm has already been done to save most of them.

On the other hand, the only well-known marsupial found native outside of Australia is something of an expert at survival. It has lasted 80 million years without changing at all, and has met the challenge of placental mammals nobly. This is the American opossum, which may be dull-witted but certainly knows how to endure.

In Cretaceous times opossums large and small roved

the Americas—including some as big as ponies. About 30 million years ago, opossums seem to have disappeared from North America, but they remained in South America and eventually found their way north again many millions of years later. Today there is one North American kind of opossum and a few South American species, somewhat smaller. Generally, the American opossum has changed much less over the past epochs than any of the Australian marsupials.

Captain John Smith gave the opossum its name. He found opossums in Virginia in 1612, and was told by the Indians that they called it "*possum*," with a grunt before the name. In their language that meant "white face." So John Smith called it the *opossum*. A few years later the English geographer Samuel Purchas described the animal like this: "The Opassum hath a head like a Swine, a tayle like a Rat, as big as a Cat, and hath under her belly a bag, wherein she carrieth her young. . . . It hath the bodie of a Fox, handed and footed like a Monkey."

The opossum is about the size of a cat. Its nose is long, and its tail is hairless and scaly. With a brain only a quarter the size of a cat's, the opossum is a stupid creature, not much smarter than most reptiles. Usually it stays out of sight during the day, making its den in a hollow log, a cave, or any other small, dark place. Sometimes a confused opossum can be seen wandering through a forest in the daytime, plodding slowly along and blinking nearsightedly.

Opossums are rugged. They live in the eastern half of the United States and Canada, where winter temperatures go well below zero and summer temperatures may top one hundred. Such extremes of weather do not bother them, and they remain active all winter long, unlike such hibernating animals as bears. Their chief food is insects, but they will eat snails, lizards, snakes, birds, fish, or almost anything else available. Being unfussy eaters has greatly helped the opossums to survive. An opossum can always find something it is willing to eat.

When the breeding season comes, the opossum shows its marsupial nature. The baby opossums remain inside the mother's body only thirteen days (as compared with sixty-three days for cats). Then the litter emerges. As many as twenty-five young opossums may be born at once. It takes only a few minutes for them all to appear. The newborn ones are about half an inch long and weigh practically nothing. They cannot see, and the only parts of their bodies they can use are their front feet. A scientist who has watched the birth of opossums writes: "The emerging young swing their forelimbs like swimmers, grabbing at the first thing they touch. For the fortunate ones this is the mother's hair. Their forefeet are so small that they can grasp only a few hairs at a time. Pulling themselves hand over hand, they climb rapidly up the mother's belly to the pouch."

Some of the young opossums get lost in their mother's fur, and never find the pouch. Others fall off her body.

These die quickly. The lucky ones complete the two-inch journey to the pouch in fifteen or twenty seconds and head for the nipples. When a baby opossum (or any kind of marsupial baby) takes its mother's nipple into its mouth, the nipple swells so that the baby is "attached" to it. It cannot let go of the nipple for many weeks. For opossums, the nursing time is about forty days. Only then can the baby open its mouth and pull away from the nipple. Soon the eyes are open, and the young opossum begins to venture outside the pouch—always crawling back in for dinner. When it is twelve weeks old, the young opossum starts nursing from outside the pouch, and a month later it is on its own.

Opossums have become living fossils for various reasons. They bring forth many offspring, and seven to nine survive from each litter—a high rate of reproduction. They are able to withstand extremes of climate. They make their homes anywhere and eat anything. Their flesh has a bitter taste, so that most meat-eating animals leave them alone. The opossum is slow and clumsy, and can hardly defend itself at all, but it has one good trick that helps it when trouble arrives: "playing possum." It lies down and pretends to be dead. Most enemies quickly lose interest in it.

Somehow these traits have been enough to let the opossum withstand the effects of time. Alone among North American marsupials, it is still with us today, and shows no sign of becoming extinct. In South America its marsupial cousins also thrive—the woolly opossum of Uruguay, the thick-tailed opossum of Paraguay and Argentina, the water opossum of Central America and Brazil, and others. One other kind of marsupial, not an opossum, is found in the Andes Mountains: *Coenolestes*, a shrewlike insect-eater.

These, plus the pouched ones of Australia, are the only marsupials left today. Everywhere else, the placental mammals have won the race for survival. The marsupials are true living fossils. But another group of mammals has also escaped extinction in Australia, even stranger and more primitive than the marsupials. They stand one notch closer to the reptile ancestors from which all mammals evolved.

They are the egg-laying mammals—the platypus and the echidna. They seem as if they were invented by a zoologist having a nightmare. Even now, almost two centuries after they were discovered, it is hard to believe that such creatures exist. A close view of them will reveal how unusual they are.

Eight: MAMMALS THAT LAY EGGS

NOVEMBER IS A SUMMER MONTH in Australia. So it was in the summer of 1797 that an Australian gentleman, whose name has not been recorded, caught a small furry animal in a pond near his home. It was a baffling-looking beast, like most of the animals being discovered in Australia at that time—but this was more baffling than most. He sent the skin to London for scientific study.

Dr. George Shaw of the British Museum received it in 1799. He had to make an effort to believe it was real.

What he saw looked like a mammal, for it had fur, and only mammals have fur. But it had the webbed feet of a duck, and large flat duck-bill to match. Furry bird or duck-billed mammal? Dr. Shaw decided it was a mammal, though an odd one. He gave it the scientific name of *Platypus anatinus*, meaning "flat-footed ducklike creature."

It happened that the name *Platypus* had been used some six years before to classify a genus of small beetles. A German scientist pointed this out, and, since when a name has once been used for some sort of animal it cannot be given to another, he furnished the duck-billed one with a new name. He called it *Ornithorhynchus paradoxus*, "the puzzling bird-beaked one." So "platypus" became the common name of the new animal, and *Ornithorhynchus* its scientific name.

Soon a second specimen arrived in England. This was not just a skin but a whole platypus, preserved in alcohol. It got careful attention from the scientists. They reported that it was about a foot long, with soft, dark-brown beaverlike fur, small eyes hidden in the pelt, and sharp claws on the webbed feet. When they began to examine the internal structure of the platypus, though, new surprises appeared.

Except for the beak, platypus looked like a mammal —from the outside. But mammals are milk-producing animals. Though the new specimen was a female platypus, it apparently lacked any trace of milk glands! Also, mammals have one passage through which the young are born, and a second passage for getting rid of body wastes. Amphibians, reptiles, and birds use a single passages for both purposes. And so, it developed, did platypus. It began to look more than ever as if platypus were no mammal at all, but a bird that mysteriously was covered with thick fur.

Platypus

In 1824, a German scientist destroyed that theory. He showed that the platypus did have milk glands after all, so small that earlier men had failed to notice them. On the other hand, it was now thought certain that platypus was an egg-laying creature. Could a mammal lay eggs? Would an egg-laying animal give milk? Where did this impossible animal fit into the scheme of classification, anyway?

The situation became more complicated when a second misfit was discovered in Australia. This was an animal that the settlers called the "native porcupine" or the "spiny anteater." It had a long toothless snout, spines instead of fur, and the same single opening for egg-laying and waste disposal that the platypus had. Instead of webbed feet, the spiny anteater had flat big-clawed ones, and the hind feet were turned almost backward. The milk glands seemed to be missing at first, though a close look showed that they were there but extremely small. Somehow this animal picked up a Greek name, *echidna*, which means "viper." Its scientific name, *Tachyglossus*, was more accurate. The name, a description of its feeding method, means "swift tongue."

The echidna did not look very much like the platypus, but they seemed to be at least distantly related to each other, and neither of them was related to any other animal whatever. Because they had no teeth, both were classed at the start with the order of anteaters. That seemed wrong to most zoologists, who put them in a special new order, *Monotremata* ("animals with one opening"). They still were not sure whether that order belonged in the phylum of mammals or the phylum of reptiles. Which was easier to accept—an egg-laying mammal or a furry, milk-producing reptile?

More information on the living habits of the two monotremes was needed. No one had ever seen a platypus or an echidna actually laying eggs, hatching them, or nursing its young. Some scientists did not believe the milk glands could really be used for that purpose, for how could an animal with a hard, horny beak possibly nurse? Other scientists went on thinking the platypus was just a clever hoax. They said scornfully that cunning Chinese craftsmen had glued a duck's bill to some kind of mole to create confusion for English zoologists.

As new specimens were captured, these objections died down. The platypus was no hoax, for reputable scientists had seen it alive. As for the bill, it was not hard and horny at all. The early platypuses had arrived in London with the bills dried out. On a live platypus, the bill was soft and rubbery, flexible and sensitive. Even so, it still was difficult to understand how a baby platypus could suckle.

Excitement arose in 1829 when the discovery of four platypus eggs was announced. Unhappily, a close look showed them to be actually tortoise eggs. Two years later, a naval officer named Maule explored a platypus nest and found broken eggshells, though that still did not prove that the eggs had been laid by a platypus. Lieutenant Maule also squeezed the belly of a female platypus to prove that the milk glands really did produce milk, or something similar to milk.

An English zoologist, George Bennett, went to Australia in 1832 to study the platypus in its native surroundings. He solved the riddle of how the young ones nurse, by showing that the mother's milk flows from the glands down her belly, and is simply licked by the young. But he could find no platypus eggs, so the puzzle of how the platypus reproduces remained a puzzle a while longer.

George Bennett was also the first man to raise platypuses in captivity. He caught two young ones and kept them alive for five weeks in 1858. Bennett watched them "playing like a couple of puppies," nipping at each other with their beaks, wrestling, tumbling one over the other. "Now and then," he wrote, "they would even make friends with me. I stroked or scratched them; they enjoyed being petted and snapped playfully at my fingers—just like puppies."

The question of how a platypus is born remained open for twenty-six more years. In 1884, the matter was settled when an English zoologist, Dr. W. H. Caldwell, went to Australia to beard the platypus in its lair. Dr. Caldwell succeeded where all earlier researchers had failed. He observed a platypus laying eggs. Almost at the same time, an Austrian zoologist named Wilhelm Haacke, who had come to Australia to study the echidna, caught a female who seemed to have something in her pouch. (Echidnas and platypuses, like other Australian mammals, are equipped with pouches.) Dr. Haacke reached carefully into the echidna's pouch, expecting to find baby echidnas—and found an egg. The two scientists had proved at last that the monotremes occupied a position midway between reptiles and mammals. They laid eggs—and then nursed their young.

The British Association for the Advancement of Science was holding a meeting at Montreal that year. On September 2, 1884, the assembled scientists received a telegram from Dr. Caldwell in Australia. He wasted no words. The telegram read:

MONOTREMES OVIPAROUS OVUM
MEROBLASTIC CALDWELL

That may have seemed like a code message to the telegraph operator, but it meant a great deal to the world of science. Translated into ordinary English, the message read: "Monotremes lay eggs; the eggs are soft-shelled."

The mystery was solved. Echidnas and platypuses are mammals of an extremely primitive kind, even more a throwback to ancient days than the marsupials. They survive from a time when reptiles were evolving into the earliest mammals, and they show a mixture of reptilelike and mammal-like features.

They are warm-blooded, but their body temperature averages only 82 degrees, much lower than in other mammals. Though they nurse their young, they do not produce true milk, but rather a thick cheesy substance. Their hearts, brains, ears, and blood vessels follow many reptilian traits. And, of course, they reproduce like reptiles, by laying eggs.

The platypus is found only in southeastern Australia today. As its webbed feet show, it lives along the banks of rivers and streams, feeding on water-dwelling plants and animals, using its ducklike bill to dig worms and shrimps from river mud. The appetite of the platypus is enormous. Each twenty-four hours it needs half its own weight in food to keep alive. A pair of the animals kept in an Australian zoo had to be fed 1,200 earthworms, fifty crayfish, and smaller numbers of grubs, tadpoles, and beetles every day!

Home, for the platypus, is a deep burrow along a riverbank. It uses its strong claws to hollow out several rooms that it lines with leaves and moss. The burrow may be as much as sixty feet long, with barriers placed along it to block an invading enemy. Though the female has a pouch, it is too small to use in raising the young. She lays two soft-shelled dirty-white eggs at a time, and the young ones live in a round nest of grass and leaves after they hatch. When they are eleven weeks old their eyes open, and a month later they leave the nest and take to the water for the first time. The mother platypus lies on her back to nurse her babies, which press the "milk" from her nipples by nudging them with their beaks. Those beaks contain teeth which look remarkably like the teeth of mammals that lived more than 100 million years ago. They disappear when a platypus reaches adulthood.

Like many living fossils, the platypus tends to be shy and retiring. It stays hidden by day, and moves about warily after dark. When trouble approaches, it burrows quickly into the mud. The males have sharp poisonous spines on their hind legs, which can inflict painful injuries, but the platypus would rather hide than fight any time.

The echidna, or spiny anteater, is not so startling to

Echidna

behold as a platypus, since it has no feature as strange as the ducklike bill. It is not an ordinary-looking animal, though, with its thick spines, its long snout, and its turned-around hind feet. An echidna looks something like a hedgehog that has been carelessly designed.

It lives in mountainous country in many parts of Australia and also on the neighboring islands of Papua and New Guinea. Insects are its chief food; it laps them up with its long, sticky tongue. The strong claws help it to dig into ant nests on raiding trips. It can also burrow rapidly when attacked; surrounded by dogs, it will dig its way into the ground, leaving only its spiny back exposed. Where digging is impossible, the echidna rolls into a tight ball, its soft parts hidden and its spines outward.

The echidna lays only one egg at a time, and puts it in its pouch for storage. After the baby hatches, it continues to live in the pouch for some weeks, nursed by its mother. Otherwise, the echidna's body functions much like that of the platypus. There is the same mixture of reptile and mammal about the internal organs, and the skeleton has many features shown by no other mammals but common in reptiles.

The echidna and the platypus appear to be the last remnants of the earliest group of mammals that evolved. They are closest to the reptilian way of life. About 100 million or 150 million years ago, the mammals branched into two groups, the egg-layers and the marsupials. Later the marsupials gave rise to the placental mammals. Most of the egg-layers died out. Only these two, living in burrows on a continent of ancient creatures, were able to survive.

At least, so we think. We have very little fossil evidence to back our beliefs so far. The monotremes *must* be an ancient type of mammal, or else the whole story of mammal evolution is wrong. However, no truly ancient monotreme fossils have yet been discovered. The earliest fossil platypus remains are only about a million years old. They include a giant form five feet long. The rest of the fossil record, stretching back to the dawn of the era of mammals, is still missing.

The duck-billed platypus and its single relative, the echidna, are evolutionary misfits. Like *Peripatus*, the hoatzin, the tuatara, and some of our other living fossils, they stand midway between one evolutionary group and the next. Of all the odd and curious creatures that live in "the attic of the world," Australia, these warm-blooded egg-layers are certainly the strangest.

Nine: SOME PUZZLING ANTEATERS

MONOTREMES AND MARSUPIALS are not the only primitive mammals that exist as living fossils today. A tribe of toothless, long-snouted creatures found on many continents also traces its ancestry back to epochs long gone. They are the *insectivores*, or "insect-eaters," and they include some puzzling anteaters that are living fossils in every way.

We have to talk about the *aardvark* first, because any animal with a name spelled that way must naturally lead all the rest. Aardvarks are familiar to anyone who has ever tried to read an encyclopedia or a dictionary from the beginning. But they are not so common outside the pages of reference books.

The name is Dutch, and means "earth pig." That name was provided by the Boers, the Dutch-descended settlers of South Africa, not because an aardvark looks much like a pig but because its meat, salted or smoked, tastes rather like pork. The scientific name is *Orycteropus,* which means "the digger."

The aardvark could well have been made up out of leftover animal parts. Its enormously long nose ends in a flat circle, like a pig's; its ears are like a donkey's; its tail is like a kangaroo's. Just when the Boers made the acquaintance of the aardvark we do not know, but the earliest published report dates from 1719. A German pastor named Peter Kolb published a bulky volume in that year called *Description of the Cape of Good Hope,* devoted to the natives and the natural history of what is now the Republic of South Africa. In the section called "On the Pigs," Kolb wrote of the "earth pig" as follows:

"It somewhat resembles the red pigs one meets in some places in Europe. But it has a longer skull and sharper snout, but no teeth [Kolb means tusks] and few bristles. The tail is long, the legs are long and strong. It lives in the ground where it makes a burrow with great speed. As soon as it has its head and forelimbs in the hole, it can hold on so fast that even the strongest man cannot pull it out. Should it be hungry, it will look for an ant-hill. When it has found one, it looks around [to see] whether there is any danger . . . then it lies down and extends its tongue as far as it can. The ants crawl upon the tongue. When there are enough, the animal pulls the tongue in and swallows them. Its flesh has a delicious taste, almost like that of our wild hogs, and is very healthy."

Kolb's description was accurate in most ways. He should have said that the South African aardvark feeds on termites, not on ants; and the aardvark is not really without teeth. It has unusual rootless teeth, tube-shaped and very soft and weak.

Aardvark

Though Kolb was a trustworthy observer, European scientists did not want to believe in his "earth pig." Not until a later explorer brought back more information in 1766 did the aardvark officially go into the zoology books. Eventually it was discovered that there were three kinds of aardvark: the South African one, five to six feet long; a larger one that lives in the jungles of central Africa; and a smaller one from northeastern Africa. That third one remained unknown to science until 1862, when a traveler named Theodor Heuglin discovered it. He wrote:

"Although the long narrow head, containing little brain, and the dull eyes give the animal a rather stupid appearance, it is very nimble and lively, likes to play, makes comical jumps into the air and turns round on itself using its powerful tail as a support. Its posture is generally kangaroo-like; it frequently walks on its hind legs only, rests with doubled-up body on its tail, lowers its head vertically to the ground and lays back its long ears like a hare."

Heuglin was able to keep aardvarks in captivity. He said, "They soon got to know me and followed me about like dogs." He reported that aardvarks spend the day sleeping in deep burrows, coming out at night to search for the termite nests where they find their meals. Their big claws can demolish a termite hill with ease.

An aardvark faced with enemies will use those claws to dig its way out of trouble. If it has time, it will burrow into the ground in a hurry, as Peter Kolb observed. An aardvark can dig faster than two strong men with shovels. If necessary, aardvarks can run, or rather hop, leaping along swiftly if not very gracefully on their hind legs. There is one report of an aardvark who was able to outrun a lion this way.

For many years, scientists were at a loss for a way to classify this big, unlikely-looking creature. Though strong and swift, it fed only on insects, and it burrowed in the ground like some tiny, helpless rodent. Some zoologists grouped it with certain other anteaters, but the relationship was not at all close. Then, in 1888, came the discovery of a fossil aardvark on the Greek island of Samos. Though millions of years old, it was almost identical to the modern aardvark. Now it was seen that aardvarks were living fossils, whose closest animal kin were probably extinct.

The discovery of other fossils has helped to fit the aardvark into the evolutionary picture a little better. In 1918, one zoologist made the guess that aardvarks were highly primitive members of the group of mammals known as *ungulates*, the hoofed animals. Some of the most familiar ungulates are horses, sheep, pigs, cattle, and deer. Twenty years later, a fossil mammal was found in New Mexico that indeed seemed to link the aardvark to the ungulates. Its general appearance was that of an aardvark, but its feet placed it with the hoofed mammals.

An even older fossil from Europe is a giant aardvark the size of a rhinoceros, with huge digging claws, curved as in the modern aardvark. So the theory today is that the ancestors of the aardvark belonged to the ungulate group, but took a different evolutionary turn. While most of the ungulates were evolving hooves, the aardvark remained almost unchanged—armed with claws for digging, instead. Its teeth, its bones, its brain structure, almost everything about it—all show that the aardvark comes to us across the ages from an era when mammals were very different from those of today.

Africa is the home of another insect-eating mystery mammal, the *pangolin.* Four species of pangolin live there: the long-tailed, white-bellied, black-bellied, and giant pangolins. Three other species come from Asia: the Indian, Chinese, and Malayan pangolins.

At first glance the pangolin does not look like any sort of mammal at all. It resembles a huge brown pine cone. But pine cones do not have legs or eyes, and when a pangolin stirs it shows that it belongs to the Animal Kingdom. It is often thought to be some kind of large lizard with big scales. However, underneath the thick, horny scales there lives a warm-blooded mammal. The scales are actually bunches of hair that have grown together.

The pangolin—sometimes called the scaly anteater—is not new to zoology. The Chinese thought it was a fish, and called it "dragon-carp." An ancient Chinese naturalist wrote: "The dragon-carp is so called because its scales resemble those of a dragon. It raises these scales and waits until a number of insects have gathered between them, attracted by the scent it gives off. Then it suddenly claps them together, kills the insects and eats them." It was a very imaginative theory, and the only thing wrong with it is that the pangolin does not behave that way. It gobbles up termites and other insects like that equally strange living fossil, the aardvark, using its mouth.

The Romans knew of the pangolin, but thought it was an "earth crocodile," a reptile. Claudius Aelianus, who lived about A.D. 200, wrote that it "is the size of a small dog. Its skin is armed with such a rough and closely knit bark that when it has been stripped off it serves for arrows and can even pierce brass and iron." Again, fancy seems to have triumphed over fact here.

More reliable is the account of the eighteenth-century French traveler, Desmarchais. He told of a four-footed animal from the forests of Guinea, called *quoggelo* by the natives. "It is covered from the neck to the tip of its tail with scales," he wrote. "They are shaped very much like the leaves of artichokes only somewhat more pointed. They lie close together and are thick and strong

Pangolin

enough to protect the animal from the claws and teeth of other animals which attack it."

Desmarchais described how the pangolin curls up tightly when caught by a leopard, wrapping its scaly tail over its belly. The leopard turns the curled-up pangolin over, nudging it with its paws, but cuts itself on the sharp scales when it tries to open it. "They leave it in peace," Desmarchais concluded.

No one is quite sure of the pangolin's place in the evolutionary story. It lacks teeth, always a sign that a mammal is quite primitive. Its diet, therefore, is one of insects. But it is not related to the aardvark or to the anteaters of South America. Its scaly covering seems to link it to another armored beast, the armadillo, but again there is no connection. The pangolin, like the aardvark, stands alone.

The fossil record is not helpful. Some incomplete fossils of pangolinlike animals about 20 million years old have been found in Europe. From the North America of 70 million years ago come certain very primitive mammals that may be ancestors of the pangolin. Otherwise the record is still blank. We know that the pangolin is a creature overlooked by evolution. This "walking pine cone" must have existed in something like its present form millions of years ago. But the details of the story remain a puzzle.

South America, which is nearly as rich in animal antiques as Australia, gives us another outlandish-looking insect-eater. This, the anteater, is also toothless and long-snouted. An anteater looks like nothing else on earth—except another anteater.

The giant anteater, also called "ant bear," is about two feet tall and six or seven feet long, tail included. The anteater's head is mostly snout, a huge, tapering muzzle that contains a tongue up to sixteen inches long. The mouth is just large enough to let this tongue flicker out. The eyes, ears, and nose are all tiny, and so is the anteater's brain.

Like the aardvark and the pangolin, the giant anteater has a set of powerful claws. To keep them sharp, the anteater tucks them back under its wrists when it walks, putting its weight on the upper sides of the feet instead of on the soles. The animal is quite comfortable walking on its knuckles this way, and the important claws are never dulled by scraping along the ground.

The anteater's large, bushy tail makes up about a third of the animal's length. The tail may be dragged along behind, but usually it is lifted and draped squirrel-fashion over the anteater's back. Some naturalists

Anteater

say that the tail serves as an umbrella in the rainy forests where the anteater lives. It is also used to brush away bothersome insects.

Ants and termites by the thousand keep these animals nourished. In the tropical plain country of British Guiana and Venezuela, termite hills a dozen feet high are found. The anteater claws a hole in the hill and goes to work with its long, swift, sticky tongue. William Dampier, the seventeenth-century English pirate, told how anteaters sometimes put their noses flat against the ground and stick their tongues out. Passing ants crawl across it and are trapped. "In two or three minutes," Dampier wrote, the tongue "will be covered all over with the ants," and the anteater then draws in its tongue and enjoys its meal. (Peter Kolb had made the same observation about the unrelated aardvark.) "They smell very strong of ants," Dampier noted, "and taste much stronger; for I have eaten of them."

Anteaters are good swimmers. They move rapidly in the water, with just the tip of the snout and the end of the tail above the surface. For all their clumsy appearance they climb trees well, too, and even scramble over high walls on their nightly prowls.

Like many of the living fossils we have met so far, anteaters keep out of sight by day, and try to go unnoticed as much as possible at night—a difficult trick for such an eye-catching beast. They are peaceful by nature, though termites probably would not agree. Their long, sharp claws and powerful front legs give them their only means of defense, since they have no way of biting an enemy, lack the body armor of a pangolin, and are too slow to escape by running.

When faced with attack, an anteater rarely tries to climb a tree or burrow to safety in the manner of an aardvark. Instead it rears on its hind legs and lashes out with its claws. It can slash a hunting dog to death, and has even been known to inflict serious wounds on a jaguar. The anteater is hunted by some Indian tribes of South America, who regard its meat as a delicacy, and they too feel the anteater's strength. Cases are known of hunters who have been killed by large anteaters who claw at them or crush them with their muscular forearms.

The giant anteater, though it is not related to the pangolin or the aardvark, has two things in common with those African animals: its fondness for termites and its nightmarish appearance. "Why, sometimes I've believed as many as six impossible things before breakfast," the White Queen tells Alice in *Through the Looking-Glass,* but even the White Queen would find it taxing to believe in these long-nosed beasts.

Ten: FOSSILS OF THE FOREST

NOT MANY OF THE FAMILIAR large mammals of our day can be called living fossils. Horses, deer, cattle, bears, elephants, and others have only a short history in their present forms. Evolution has worked great changes in them over the last few million years.

If we could turn back time, we would find many strange ancestors of the modern mammals. A visit to 50 million years ago would show us horses a foot high. We could go back 40 million years to see the earliest elephants, which had not yet evolved their long trunks. Going back 20 million years, we might encounter a rhinoceros as tall as a three-story building, or a pig bigger than a present-day horse.

But we do not have to take a trip in time to view the ancestor of the giraffe. It can be seen—alive—in zoos throughout the world. It is the *okapi,* a living fossil of

Okapi

the African jungle. When it was discovered, at the beginning of this century, it caused a sensation like that touched off in 1938 by the coelacanth.

We have already mentioned the fossil background of the okapi. Scientists digging in Greece early in the nineteenth century had found the bones of an extinct animal they called *Helladotherium*, which looked like a giraffe with a short neck. Later came the discovery of a closely related fossil form, *Samotherium*, on the Greek island of Cyprus. When Charles Darwin published his *Origin of Species* in 1859, he suggested that the giraffe must have evolved from an early short-necked form. The long neck had developed because it aided the animal to reach a better food supply on the top branches of trees. So the discovery of the fossil short-necked animals was a point in favor of Darwin's theory.

But no one expected a live *Helladotherium* or *Samotherium* to turn up.

The first clue came from Henry Stanley, the man who went looking for Dr. Livingstone in Africa. When his book *In Darkest Africa* appeared in 1890, Stanley wrote of a "donkey" of the Congo jungle, called *atti* by the natives. "They say that they sometimes catch them in pits," Stanley remarked. "They eat leaves."

No one before had ever heard of leaf-eating forest donkeys in Africa. The closest thing to a member of the horse family in the Congo was the zebra. But zebras did not live in the thick jungle where the atti was said to dwell. Zebras were animals of the open plains.

So most experts wrote Stanley's comment off as a mistake. One who did not was Sir Harry Johnston, the governor of Uganda. Sir Harry, who knew Henry Stanley, believed that many unknown animals remained to be discovered in the jungles. When a band of pygmies from the Congo arrived in Uganda, Sir Harry questioned them about Stanley's atti.

"They at once understood what I meant," Sir Harry wrote. The pygmies told him that Stanley had heard the name wrong; it was not atti, but *o-api* or *okapi.* They described it as "dark gray all over the upper parts of the body, with stripes on the belly and legs."

Sir Harry accompanied the pygmies back to the Congo. The Congo then belonged to Belgium, and when he arrived at the outpost of Fort Mbeni, Sir Harry questioned the Belgian officers stationed there. They said they had never seen an okapi alive, but they knew that the natives hunted them in the forest. He wrote, "At first they excited me by declaring that there was a skin lying about which I could have; eventually it was found that the skin had been cut up by their native soldiers to be made into waist-belts. . . ."

The Belgians managed to find two strips of okapi skin for Sir Harry. His Congo visit yielded nothing else, not even a glimpse of the animal. When he left, a Belgian official promised to send him a complete okapi skin and skull.

Sir Harry sent the two strips of okapi skin to England, where they were shown at the December 1900 meeting of the Zoological Society of London. The scientists thought a new type of zebra had been discovered. They gave it a temporary name of *Equus johnstoni*, with a question mark after the *Equus*.

The Congo official kept his word and sent Sir Harry an okapi hide and two skulls, early in 1901. Sir Harry realized the truth about the animal now. As he wrote, "Upon receiving this skin, I saw at once what the okapi was—namely, a close relation of the giraffe."

A clear picture of the animal emerged. It was as big as a medium-sized horse, with long ears and a long tongue. Its legs were marked with stripes. The shape of its teeth, skull, and hooves all showed its kinship with the giraffe. It even had the little bumplike horns of the giraffe, hidden under the skin of its forehead.

Sir Harry sent his new specimens to London, and the okapi was promptly removed from the zebra clan. Since it looked so much like the fossil *Helladotherium*, some zoologists wanted to call it *Helladotherium* also. However, that extinct animal had not had horns, and its teeth were different from the okapi's. The okapi was more like the other fossil, *Samotherium*, but there were slight differences there too. Finally a new genus was named for the discovery—*Okapia*. The animal found by Sir Harry Johnston became *Okapia johnstoni*.

A living fossil had appeared. The okapi was almost a twin of its extinct and slightly larger ancestor, *Samotherium*. It was possible to see how another branch of the family had grown long necks and stiltlike legs to become the giraffes—but here was a surviving member of the original stock. How had it remained?

One reason was the climate of its home territory. It lived in a rain-soaked forest where few hunters cared to go. Sir Harry Johnston wrote that "the atmosphere of the forest was almost unbreathable with its Turkish-bath heat, its reeking moisture, and its powerful smell of decaying, rotting vegetation. We seemed, in fact, to be transported back to Miocene times, to an age and a climate scarcely suitable for the modern type of real humanity." In that steaming heat, a sort of "lost world" existed, a sanctuary for many strange forms of life.

Now that the secret of the okapi was out, several expeditions went to the Congo to find specimens. The New York Zoological Society was eager to have a live okapi in its Bronx Zoo. Herbert Lang of the New York Zoological Society reached the Congo in 1909 and entered the okapi's forest, which he called "the most unhealthy country in the world." He wrote that the okapi "inhabits a narrow strip some seven hundred miles long and hardly one hundred forty miles wide, about seven hundred miles from either coast." Few men, white or black, dared to enter here. According to Lang, "it is one of the most dismal spots on the face of the globe, for the torrid sun burns above miles of leafy expanse, and the unflagging heat of about one hundred degrees day and night renders the moist atmosphere unbearable. Over the whole area storms of tropical violence thunder and rage almost daily."

Lang's men captured a young okapi. It was friendly and tame, and ate condensed milk. But the milk supply ran out, and the okapi died before more could be obtained. Later, Lang had more success with okapis. He studied them in their home grounds, and was able to show that the okapi had not always lived in swampy tropical jungles. Once it had been a creature of the plains, as the giraffe is today. But in time it was crowded out by animals better suited to life in the open, and it took refuge in the remote, humid heart of the dark Congo.

Another mammal that escaped the scythe of time is the tapir, a peculiar-looking beast that seems to be a cross between a pig, a rhinoceros, and an elephant. It has the build of a rhino, with a short neck, thick legs, and a stocky body. Instead of being a horny hide, though, its skin is like a pig's, as is the general shape of its head. The elephantlike part is the nose, which is a drooping snout four or five inches long, soft and flexible. It is a nose that seems to have wanted to turn into a trunk, but couldn't quite manage it.

As it happens, the tapir is related to all three. Like the pig, the rhino, and the elephant, it belongs to that large group of mammals called the *ungulates*, those with hooves. Most ungulates have an even number of toes. Just a few—the horse, the rhinoceros, and the tapir—have an odd number. The theory is that the more primitive an ungulate is, the more toes it will have. The horse, which is very highly evolved, has only one toe on each foot. The tapir has three toes on its hind feet, four toes on the front ones. That alone might tell us that the tapir has an ancient pedigree—but we have the fossil evidence, besides.

The oldest tapirlike fossils go back about 70 million years. The first tapirs, which lived in North America, were not very much like those of today, but the family resemblance is there. They were small, almost graceful animals. They may have been closely related to the tiny ancestors of the horse. But while the horse evolved in the direction of speed, the tapir evolved in that of bulk and strength.

Over millions of years, the tapir spread until it lived in most parts of the world. Tapir fossils have been

Tapir

found in Asia, Europe, and most parts of the United States. About 40 million years ago the tapir reached something like its present form. Fossil tapirs from the Miocene, 20 million years ago, are almost exactly like tapirs of today, with little change.

The tapir has always preferred a warm-weather home. As many parts of the world grew cooler, the tapir died out. It vanished first from Europe, then from China. About a million years ago, tapirs still lived in California, Pennsylvania, and other parts of North America. Today they are found only in Borneo, Malaya, South America, and Central America. Though they live in such widely separated regions of the world, the different species of modern tapirs are extremely similar. That shows how slow tapir evolution has been, since the tapir migration took place many millions of years ago.

The three types of South and Central American tapir were discovered by scientists several centuries ago. However, the Asiatic branch of the family was officially pronounced a myth as late as 1812.

The man who made that unwise statement was Georges Cuvier, one of the greatest of European zoologists. Cuvier had decided that all the big animals of the world had already been discovered. "There is little hope," he declared, "that we shall discover further new species of large mammals in the future." Usually when a scientist makes such a sweeping decree he ends by eating his words, and that was Cuvier's fate.

Chinese paintings and books had long portrayed a

comical-looking animal called the *mé*, black and white with a short dangling snout. Perhaps Cuvier never saw any pictures or descriptions of the mé, but if he had he would simply have dismissed it as a fairy-tale animal, an imaginary beast like the dragons forever being painted by Chinese artists. An old Chinese zoology book, describing the mé, said that "it resembles a bear; it is black and white in color, has a small head and short legs, a trunk like an elephant, eyes like a rhinoceros, the tail of a cow and the paws of a tiger." Except for the last item, that is a fair description of a tapir—but, according to Cuvier, tapirs were found only in South and Central America.

In 1772, an English explorer named Wahlfeldt saw a "two-toned rhinoceros" on the island of Java, and his drawing showed it with a long snout. It looked just like a South American tapir. Cuvier shrugged this off in 1800 by saying that Wahlfeldt had seen a young rhinoceros, and must have imagined the snout. Soon afterward, Cuvier himself dug up fossil tapirs near Paris. He admitted, a little sheepishly, that tapirs must have lived in Europe once, though they had become extinct there. He still refused to believe there were tapirs in Asia, however. With an odd sort of blindness, Cuvier made his statement of 1812 that no big mammals were likely to be discovered anywhere in the world in times to come.

The year before, an English politician and naturalist named Stamford Raffles had come to live in the East Indies. Young and energetic, Raffles was a colonizer and builder who founded the city of Singapore and helped to expand British influence in much of Southeast Asia. He also loved to collect the strange, unknown Asiatic animals that Cuvier said could not exist.

Raffles heard of a black-and-white "rhinoceros" with a snout that lived in the jungles of Sumatra. He set out to find it. On his first attempt he found a real rhinoceros, with a horn and a thick armored hide. In 1817, he discovered a second species of Asian rhinoceros. The unknown long-snouted animal remained a mystery.

Visiting India in 1818, Raffles met two French explorers named Pierre Diard and Alfred Duvaucel. They were traveling through Asia, collecting animals for the Paris zoo. Duvaucel was twenty-five years old, and happened to be the stepson of Georges Cuvier. He was in the process of doing just what his stepfather said could not be done. He had discovered a number of new species of large mammals in India, such as the *barasingha*, a type of deer.

Diard and Duvaucel were invited to visit Raffles' home, which was on the island of Sumatra. Raffles kept a marvelous private zoo there. Lovely Sumatran birds hovered on perches; apes of many sorts swung through the trees of Raffles' garden; two magnificent tame leopards allowed themselves to be stroked and petted. Raffles even had a Malay bear that had a liking for champagne.

Soon after the two Frenchmen arrived, a certain Major Farquhar paid a call on Raffles. He showed Sir Stamford the head of a long-snouted "rhinoceros" which he said he had shot twelve years before. Diard and Duvaucel recognized it as a tapir. Quietly, they drew Major Farquhar aside and questioned him. He told them that the animal "was just as common in the Indian jungle as the elephant and rhinoceros." Diard made a sketch of the head, took down the description of the creature, and sent it secretly to Cuvier in France—along with an account of all the other animals in Raffles' collection.

Diard apologized in his letter to Cuvier for having dared to discover so many new species. Speaking of the tapir, he said, "I was profoundly surprised that such a large mammal had remained unknown until now." Cuvier, to his credit, admitted his mistake. He took back his declaration of 1812 about the impossibility of finding new mammals, and published a scientific description of the Asiatic tapir based on the notes Diard and Duvaucel had sent him.

Diard and Duvaucel had not been particularly honest, They had taken advantage of Raffles' hospitality to steal his discoveries. Raffles, meanwhile, had received a live tapir. He was about to write a scientific article on the newly discovered animal when he learned that Cuvier had beaten him to it. Astonished and angry, Raffles ordered Diard and Duvaucel arrested. Diard was jailed for two years on a charge of "spying." Duvaucel, since he was Cuvier's stepson, stayed out of jail, but was shipped back to India. He made new animal finds soon after in the mountains of Central Asia, and was planning an expedition to Tibet when he died suddenly of a tropical disease at the age of thirty-two.

Today the Asiatic tapir (*Tapirus indicus*) is well known. It ranges from Siam to Sumatra and Borneo, a shy, sturdy beast that follows the wise practice of many living fossils, keeping out of sight as much as possible. Its white stripes set it off from the South American tapirs, which are entirely blackish-brown. Tapirs are land-dwelling animals, but they love water and are generally found near rivers and lakes, though one South American species lives high in the Andes.

Tapirs have very poor eyesight. One explorer who found that out to his cost was F. W. Up de Graff, who told of his tapir experiences in a book called *Head Hunters of the Amazon*, published in 1923. Once Up de Graff was traveling in a canoe along a jungle river in Brazil and went ashore to gather food. Suddenly a big tapir came bounding out of the underbrush. Scenting strangers, it darted for the water. However, Up de Graff's canoe was sitting by the riverbank. The tapir failed to see it, and landed on top of it, smashing it to bits and leaving the explorer stranded in the jungle.

On a later trip, Up de Graff and some companions were once again making a river journey by canoe. They went ashore to rest, parking the canoe at the river's edge. There came crashing and banging noises from the jungle, and then not one but *three* tapirs burst into the open—all three headed right toward the canoe! Up de Graff and his friends began to shout and wave their arms, but the nearsighted tapirs took no notice. The first one leaped over the canoe, clearing it by a nose. The second tapir made the jump with something to spare, but the third collided with the canoe, almost knocking it apart.

Not only is the tapir dull of vision, it is dull of wit as well. Its brain weighs only a thousandth as much as its entire body—another trademark of the living fossil. Evolution while leaving the tapir's shape alone for 20 million years, has also done little for its brain. Tapirs are hermitlike animals, wandering slowly and alone through the forests, browsing on leaves and shoots. In South America tapir meat is considered a delicacy, but the animals are hard to find, and hard to kill when found. They head immediately for water and duck out of sight, swimming with surprising grace and speed.

At least one South American animal makes the tapir look like a downright genius by comparison. The tree sloth is famous for its stupidity—and it is so slow-moving that plants sprout in its fur.

Two kinds of tree sloths exist today—the two-toed sloths of South America and the three-toed sloths of Central America. They are the last survivors of what was once a large and widespread family.

The first sloths appeared about 10 million years ago. They were ground-dwellers that quickly reached giant size. One kind, the *Megatherium americanum* ("giant

American mammal") was larger than an elephant. It looked something like an enormous bear covered with long coarse hair. Shambling along through the forests from Pennsylvania southward, this monster stood on its hind feet to munch leaves that grew eighteen to twenty feet above the ground. Its heavy tail served it as a prop. Another species of giant ground sloth lived in the southern states; the first known fossil specimen was discovered in a Virginia cave by Thomas Jefferson. A third species was found as far west as California. South America was the place where these huge animals originated, and they lingered there well into the age of man. There is evidence that Indians hunted giant ground sloths in Patagonia only a few thousand years ago. From time to time, there have been rumors of the discovery of a living *Megatherium* somewhere in South America, but no one has been able to prove that they still exist.

The giants may be gone, but the equally ancient tree-dwelling sloths remain. They are about as big as fair-sized dogs, and are found in an upside-down position clinging to the limbs of trees.

Sloths are considered to be relatives of the South American anteaters. Anteaters and sloths are classed together in the order *Edentata*, meaning "without teeth." Like most classifications, this one is not quite perfect. Anteaters are toothless, but sloths lack only their front teeth. A sloth's teeth are poorly developed, without roots or enamel. (Pangolins are as toothless as anteat-

Sloth

ers, but are not classed with the *Edentata*. Neither are aardvarks, which have primitive slothlike teeth. The shape of such things as the ribs, as well as the teeth, distinguish the *Edentata*.)

Tree sloths have round heads, little stubby noses, and blank eyes that give them the look of sleepwalkers. Their arms are much longer than their legs. All four limbs end in sharp curving claws. The tail is a short buttonlike projection about an inch long.

Sloths are unhappy on the ground. Their short hind legs do not mesh with their long arms, and they stumble awkwardly forward, with their bellies sagging against the ground. Young sloths are unable to walk at all; older ones have a way of pulling themselves along with their claws, but they have a hard time of it. One nineteenth-century naturalist told of a captive sloth that spent hours traveling just a few feet, gasping and panting in exhaustion. Another said that a sloth on level ground is as helpless "as a man would be who had to walk a mile on stilts upon a line of feather beds."

In the trees, though, a sloth is a different creature. It moves easily and well, though no one has ever seen a sloth hurry. Its motion has been described as "like a sailor going up a rope, hand over hand." Lazily and cautiously, sloths crawl from one branch to the next, digging their claws deep into the wood and never letting go of one bough until they are firmly hooked to another. Except when climbing, sloths cling to the undersides of the branches. "They hug the branches as if they love them," wrote the naturalist William Henry Hudson. They sleep upside down, move upside down, eat upside down, and relax upside down. If sloths daydream, they do it while hanging by their claws high above the forest floor, their backs below their bellies.

Sloths hardly ever leave the trees except by accident or when forced down by enemies. From time to time, however, the urge to take a swim comes over them. They clamber down from the branches and enter the water, often striking out across rivers a mile wide. No one can explain why the usually lazy sloths undertake these adventures. William Beebe, the naturalist and explorer, once timed a sloth as it swam across a broad river. It took three hours and twenty minutes to swim a mile. Another time, Beebe caught a sloth, marked it for identification, and set it loose. He caught it forty-eight days later. It had crossed a mile-wide river and had traveled four miles through the jungle trees on the other side.

The three-toed sloth of Central America eats only the leaves of the cecropia tree. A dozen or more sloths can often be seen in the same tree, hanging upside down as they solemnly munch away. If they stripped a cecropia completely of its leaves, the tree would probably die. But some instinct gets through to the dim minds of the sloths, and they always move on to a new tree when they have thinned the old one's leaves. Since the cecropia tree will grow only in a hot climate, and the three-toed sloth will not eat anything else, it has been difficult to keep Central American sloths alive in northern zoos. The two-toed South American sloth, on the other hand, eats almost any kind of vegetable happily—cabbage, lettuce, bananas, spinach, carrots, even potatoes. South American sloths thus have done well in zoos, though, since they sleep most of the time, they do not make a particularly interesting exhibit.

Both kinds of sloth bear just one baby at a time. A nursing sloth spends its early weeks between its mother's belly and the branch to which she clings. When the mother sloth climbs, the young sloth would be uncomfortably bounced and bumped against the bough, and so it makes its way to the mother's back and hangs on with its claws hooked into her fur. "If there is anything odder than an upside-down sloth," one naturalist has written, "it must be an upside-down baby sloth hanging to the back of its upside-down parent."

Slow-moving and practically toothless, the sloth has

no way of defending itself. Its claws, though sharp, are needed to keep it hooked to its branch. How such a clumsy, harmless animal has survived so long is puzzling.

One factor that certainly has helped is the sloth's natural camouflage. Here is where the sloth's coating of plant life comes in. Evolution might have given the sloth green fur, to help it hide against the leafy background of the jungle trees. Evolution neglected to do this, but the sloth takes on a green color anyway. The fur of the sloth has tiny grooves, and small plants called *Pleurococci* make their home in them. The *Pleurococcus* is an extremely simple plant that can be seen in detail only under a microscope. Millions of them, growing in a sloth's fur, give the sloth the same color as the moss that grows on the branches of the jungle trees. Since it is such a sleepy, slow-moving, *slothful* animal, the greenish-hued sloth is hard to spot in its treetop home.

Living upside down is another special advantage. The sloth is not easy to attack, especially when it clings near the end of a branch. Its chief enemy, the jaguar, will pad out along the branch and stare in bewilderment at the sloth dangling downward, unable to find any way of reaching it.

The sloth's toughness also helps it survive. The more advanced an animal's brain is, the more easily it dies when wounded. Sloths, with their tiny brains, hardly seem to feel pain at all, and go on living even when badly clawed by a jaguar or an eagle. Wounds that would kill an ape or a man do not kill a sloth. The South American Indians, who like the taste of sloth meat, find that arrows will not kill a sloth easily. They put captured sloths to death by drowning them, but an amazingly long time is needed to drown a sloth.

It must not be very fascinating to be a sloth. But these sluggish tree-dwellers have achieved something that their monstrous cousins of the past failed to do. They have endured.

The armadillo, a living fossil found in South America, Central America, and the southern United States, is considered a close relative of the sloth and the anteater. At a quick glance, it is hard to see why. The armadillo is covered with thick armor, and looks more like a turtle than like such shaggy creatures as anteaters and sloths. But armadillos are mammals, not reptiles, despite their misleading shells. The evidence of their teeth and ribs shows that they do belong with the *Edentata.*

These armored mammals go back 20 million years or more. Ancient armadillos were much bigger than those of today. One, called a *glyptodont* ("grooved-toothed animal"), was twelve to fourteen feet long and five feet or more in height. The thick shell was made up of tough plates of bone joined together. When the glyptodont pulled in its head and huddled against the ground no enemy could make much of a dent in that sturdy shield. Some glyptodonts had tails five feet long

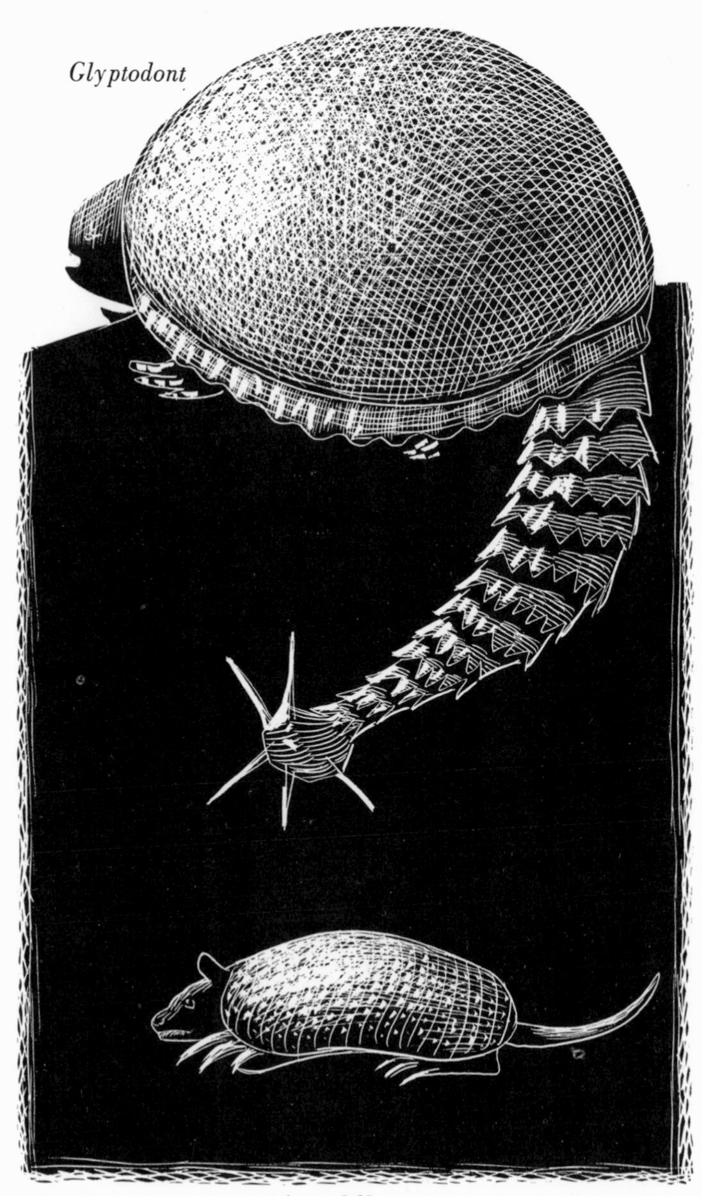

Armadillo

that ended in knobs armed with large spikes. When the glyptodont swung that wicked-looking tail like a club, it must have been almost impossible to approach.

For all its awesome armor, the glyptodont became extinct about a million years ago. A dozen different species of smaller armadillos still inhabit the world, however. They range from the giant armadillo, about three feet long and weighing a hundred pounds, down to the *pichiago*, less than six inches long from its snout to the tip of its tail. They are grouped with the sloths and anteaters because they have simple peg-shaped teeth without roots or enamel, and because their rib structure has certain primitive features not found in most other mammals.

The glyptodont's shell was one solid piece. Today's armadillos have shells made up of a number of movable bands. The most common armadillo of the United States is the nine-banded one, found in Texas and other parts of the Southwest. It weighs twelve or fifteen pounds. Other species of armadillos have from three to thirteen bands.

The entire body is protected by armor except the ears, the belly, and the insides of the legs. Many people think that an armadillo defends itself from danger by coiling itself into a tight ball, but this is not so. President Theodore Roosevelt found that out when he made an expedition to Brazil after he left the White House. He came upon two nine-banded armadillos feeding in a patch of open ground. His dogs charged, and he expected to see the armadillos roll up tight. Instead they surprised him by waddling away as fast as they could go on their little stumpy legs, and ducking into their burrows to disappear.

Only one kind of armadillo actually does roll itself up. This is the three-banded armadillo of Argentina and Brazil, known as the *apar* or *mataco*. Charles Darwin saw one in action when he visited Argentina in 1833. "It has the power of rolling itself into a perfect sphere," he wrote. "In this state it is safe from the attack of dogs; for the dog, not being able to take the whole in its mouth, tries to bite one side, and the ball slips away. The smooth hard covering of the *mataco* offers a better defense than the sharp spines of the hedgehog."

The other eleven species of armadillo run away from danger, and never try to rely on their armor. Some could not curl up if they tried; others have shells that are much softer than they look.

Like sloths and anteaters, armadillos are equipped with powerful claws on the front feet, and they rival the aardvarks when it comes to digging. An escaping armadillo can dig so fast that it seems to be sinking into the earth. Darwin told how hard it was to catch the small armadillo known as the *pichy*, or pichiciago. He saw them from horseback as he rode through the Argentinian plains, but unless he jumped from his horse within a moment, the armadillos vanished into the ground before he could dismount.

William Henry Hudson, the great naturalist and

novelist who was born of British parents in Argentina, tried to capture an armadillo when he was a boy, about 1850. There were a number of rat holes near the Hudson home, and one day workmen were pumping gas into the holes to drive out the rats. Somehow an armadillo had made his headquarters in one of the rat holes, and as young Hudson watched, the armored animal came running out and began to dig a new hole for itself, practically in front of the boy's feet.

Here was a chance to capture an armadillo and perhaps make a pet of the strange animal. Young Hudson grabbed the armadillo by its long, horny tail and started to tug. The armadillo went on digging. Hudson began to see that instead of pulling the armadillo out of the ground, he was being pulled in! As he hung tight to its tail, this creature no bigger than a cat was getting deeper and deeper into the ground. It vanished altogether, and Hudson, still gripping the tail, felt his hands being pulled into the hole, and then his wrists, and then his arms. He had to let go and admit defeat.

Armadillos eat insects, centipedes, and scorpions. According to Hudson, one species will even attack and kill snakes. That makes it the only member of the *Edentata* that eats flesh or attacks other animals.

The nine-banded armadillo almost always has four young ones at a time, and these are always identical quadruplets. Most other armadillos have one baby at a time or twins. Because of its scaly, reptilian appearance, many people think the armadillo lays eggs. But it is a true mammal, and brings forth its young alive, like all other mammals except the echidna and the platypus.

Armadillos have many natural enemies—jaguars, pumas, coyotes, dogs. Their trick of creating an instant burrow has allowed them to hold out against these marauders. Human beings also prey on the armadillo. The Indians of South and Central America are fond of its meat, and for centuries they have used its shell for baskets. Even though many armadillos are killed each year this way, they do not appear to be in danger of becoming extinct. In some places their numbers are actually increasing.

We have gone as far as we can go in our story of the living fossils of the Animal Kingdom. Starting with such lowly creatures as the sea lilies and the mollusks, we have moved from phylum to phylum, looking in on the survivors of each new phase of evolution. We have seen animals grow more complex, developing backbones, learning how to breathe air, growing feathers and hair, bringing their young ones into the world alive. From fishes to amphibians to reptiles, from reptiles to monotreme and marsupial mammals, then to the fairly recent placental mammals, the whole picture of evolution has unfolded. At each step of the way some creatures have remained to show us how things once were—coelacanth and tuatara, platypus and opossum, aardvark and sloth and tapir.

The story of living fossils of the animal world goes no

further, because we have brought it down to the last few million years. The animals that remain are newcomers. Most of the creatures in the world today arrived here only a moment ago, so to speak.

And we, who put ourselves at the top of the heap, have less place in a book of living fossils than any other animal. We have evolved more in 100,000 years than the tapir has in 20 million, the opossum in 80 million, the tuatara in 150 million, or the lowly cockroach in 350 million. The ape-man of Java, *Pithecanthropus erectus*, lived only half a million years ago, but we would telephone the zoo if we saw him on our streets today.

The hand of time is upon us. We are evolving at a fantastic rate. Even a span of a few thousand years brings great changes in mankind. We are growing taller; the shape of our skulls is changing; we are losing our body hair and such organs as the appendix. The human beings of A.D. 10,000—if we have not succeeded in blowing our planet up by then—may look back on the people of the twentieth century as primitive forms of humanity.

It is all much simpler for the living fossils. They change too, of course, for evolution leaves no species completely forgotten. But the rate of change is very different. The horseshoe crab undergoes a minor change every 50 million years or so; the cockroach, even less often. Who can dare to say what mankind will look like a mere 50 *thousand* years from now? We can guess, naturally. But we can never be sure.

The horseshoe crab can be sure, and so can *Peripatus*, and the coelacanth, and the penguin, and the armadillo, and the pangolin, and the lungfish, and the centipede. If they cared to think about it, they could have the comforting knowledge that their great-great-great-grandchildren many times over would look just about the way they themselves look.

But, of course, the living fossils do not care to think about such things, or about anything else, and we do. And that has made all the difference in the world, so far.

Eleven: LIVING FOSSILS OF THE PLANT KINGDOM

IN THE EARLIER CHAPTERS WE devoted our attention to a group of strange and curious animals. Plants, too, undergo evolution. The Plant Kingdom shows a pattern of change. Plants have risen from their simple beginnings to develop the lordly oaks and pines of our forests, the lovely roses and tulips of our gardens, the cacti of the deserts. And the course of that evolution has left us with a few "green fossils"—plants which grew when the dinosaurs lived, or even earlier, and which still grow today.

None of our garden flowers are really ancient. Neither are the trees of the woods. They evolved within the past few million years. All kinds of plant life that have flowers and seeds are quite new. Only in the simpler forms do we find the old ones.

Botanists have arranged the Plant Kingdom into phyla, just as has been done with animals. In the first chapter, we saw the phylum arrangement of the Animal Kingdom, and now we can provide the same kind of list for the plants. These are the plant phyla, beginning with the simplest:

THALLOPHYTA—*Primitive plants that are not divided into root, stem, and leaf. There are three chief groups:*

1. *Schizophyta*. One-celled plants—the bacteria.
2. *Algae*. Seaweeds and drifting water plants.
3. *Fungi*. Mushrooms and molds.

BRYOPHYTA—*Mosses and other small plants with simple stemlike and leaflike parts.*

PTERIDOPHYTA—*Ferns, which have roots, leaves, and stems.*

ARTHROPHYTA—*Plants with jointed stems, such as horsetails.*

LEPIDOPHYTA—*Plants with scalelike leaves, such as club mosses.*

SPERMATOPHYTA—*The seed-bearing plants, divided into two classes, Gymnospermae ("Naked-seeded plants") and Angiospermae ("Covered-seeded plants").*

The Gymnospermae are divided into these main orders:

1. *Cycadofilicales.* Seed ferns.
2. *Cycadales.* Sago palms and cycads.
3. *Ginkgoales.* The ginkgo tree.
4. *Gnetales.* Welwitschia, Mormon tea, and other plants with certain primitive features.
5. *Coniferales.* Fir, pine, spruce, and other cone-bearing trees.

The Angiospermae include all the flowering plants and most trees, and are divided into many orders. Since no living fossils are found in this group, we will not list the orders here.

As in the animal world, the phylum list of plants not only supplies us with a number of Greek jawbreakers, but it tells us something about the order in which plant forms developed. Since evolution works from the simple to the more complicated, we know that the seaweeds evolved before the ferns, and the ferns before the pines, and the pines before the oaks. (Note that *complicated* does not mean the same as *big*. A number of very simple plants grew to great size in the age of dinosaurs—but they were still simple plants. A tiny dandelion is more complicated than a thirty-foot-high tree fern, because of its system of producing flowers, getting them fertilized, and growing seeds. It took many millions of years for these flowering plants and trees to develop out of the older forms.)

Plant life, like animal life, began in the sea. A billion years ago or more, simple one-celled plants developed. Some were of the microscopic kind we call *bacteria.* Others belonged to the almost equally simple group known as *cyanophyceae*, "blue-green algae." The blue-green algae get their name because they are the most primitive plants that contain *chlorophyll*, that miraculous green substance that allows plants to absorb energy from sunlight.

Bacteria do not usually leave fossil remains. Blue-green algae sometimes do, surviving as shiny black films on ancient rocks. The study of such films on rocks more than half a billion years old leads botanists to think that the blue-green algae have not changed very much through the ages. They are our oldest plant living fossils.

During the Devonian Period, about 350 million years ago, both plants and animals began to leave the sea for the land. While scorpions, centipedes, and a few adventurous fish were experimenting with breathing air, small plants were making the big jump also. The first to arrive on land were the flat, scaly ones known as *lichens.* These very simple plants could take a foothold on the bare rock that we believe was all that existed in the part of the world above the sea. Anchored to the rocks, the lichens helped to turn stone into soil. These tough plants still exist, and can be seen as a grayish or greenish coating on rocks in many parts of the world.

Once there was soil, larger and more complicated plants could develop. The next to appear were the *psilophytes.* They have long been extinct, but they were the ancestors of all the land plants of later eras.

These psilophytes grew from fleshy, creeping runners that sent up stems at short distances from one another. Most of them were leafless, but a few of the forked stems sprouted flat, scalelike overlapping leaves. We can imagine the early Devonian landscape as a forlorn-looking place. Mostly, the earth's crust was bare, with lichens clinging to the rocks here and there, and algae living in small pools. Wherever they could, the psilophytes grew, raising foot-high stems toward the sunlight.

In the warm, moist climate, the early plants developed swiftly. Some psilophytes grew to heights of two feet or more, and had woody stems half an inch thick. At the tips of the little branches were long pods containing the spores that carried psilophytes through the world.

Spores should not be confused with seeds, though they both play the same role in the plant world. Seeds are produced only by plants of the highest phylum. They each contain a miniature baby plant wrapped in a protective jacket. Spores are much smaller, just barely visible to the naked eye, and give little or no protection

Psilophytes *Lichen*

to the new plant within. The higher plants have sexes just as animals do, and seeds are produced when a male cell fertilizes a female cell. The spore-producing plants are all of one sex and fertilization is not needed.

Though the psilophytes are gone, they have left two near relatives as living fossils. Both are found only in tropical countries. They are *Tmesipteris*, from the Philippines and New Zealand, and *Psilotum*, which lives in the Americas from Florida southward. They are tiny stiff-stemmed plants with scalelike leaves, and are classed with the ferns.

A living fossil often used as a Christmas decoration is ground cedar, which looks like a miniature evergreen tree. Just a few inches high, it has a straight stem with bushy side branches covered with flattened leaves. It is found in forests, often growing on the floor beneath the real evergreens that it resembles. Another Christmas favorite is ground pine, with sharp, needlelike leaves. A third is running pine, whose stems run along the ground for ten feet or more.

None of these little plants belongs to the family of evergreen trees. They come from a group of plants that was ancient long before the first pine tree sprouted—the club mosses. There are more than a hundred different kinds of club moss, most of them found in tropical countries. About twenty types grow in the eastern United States, though some are becoming rare because thoughtless people pick them so heavily at Christmas time.

If you can find a rich damp forest where the club

mosses grow thickly, you can test your imagination by sprawling out flat in their midst. By looking straight ahead, keeping your eyes only inches from the ground, and ignoring the towering trees all around, you can pretend that you are in a forest of tree-sized club mosses.

You would not have to pretend, if you found yourself thrown back 300 million years in time. Swamps covered most of the world then, and club mosses grew to giant size. Great forests of them were found throughout what is now the eastern United States. One was *Lepidodendron,* "scaly tree," which was up to fifty feet tall and had a trunk several feet thick. *Lepidodendron* had only a few branches, whose tips were covered with short, pointed leaves. The bare trunk was marked with rows of

Ground Cedar *Ground Pine* *Tmesipteris* *Psilotum*

diamond-shaped scars where fallen leaves had been attached. Another giant club moss was *Sigillaria,* with leaves three feet long.

These scaly trees became even bigger in the period known as the Pennsylvanian, about 250 million years ago. That was the time when cockroaches grew six inches long and dragonflies had thirty-inch wingspreads. In the Pennsylvanian, *Lepidodendron* and *Sigillaria* reached heights of two hundred feet. Though they were so huge, they were still simple plants, botanically speaking, because they reproduced by spores. In later ages, when the swamp conditions disappeared, the giant club mosses became extinct, leaving only the small ones we know today.

Sigillaria *Lepidodendron*

Also found in the giant swamp forests of the Pennsylvanian Period were the huge leafless trees called horsetails. They had no branches; a single hollow stem rose sixty to one hundred feet, three feet thick at the base. The horsetails were divided into jointed sections, each one a little smaller than the section below it. The places where the sections joined were marked with little scaly leaves, looking like a circle of teeth fringing the stem. The horsetails grew in dense thickets that probably looked something like the bamboo thickets of tropical countries today.

Those horsetails are gone, but it is not hard to imagine how they must have looked. Their descendants are still with us, exactly like them except in size. Horsetails can be found in damp woods, though some types like drier places. The cinders and ashes of railroad embankments often bristle with clumps of horsetails. They rarely grow more than three feet tall today, though in South America there is a horsetail that reaches heights of thirty to forty feet.

Horsetails produce shoots of two very different forms. Early in the spring the reproductive stems appear. These are tan and scaly, and are topped by a single yellow cone containing spores. When the stem is eight or ten inches high, the cone opens, and clouds of spore dust are released. The fertile stems then begin to wither, and the horsetail starts to send up the familiar green stems, with their whorls of scaly leaves. These shoots, which are sterile, live through the summer.

Related to the horsetails are the scouring rushes, sturdy, canelike plants that have a particularly prehistoric appearance. These stiff, branchless plants, sometimes six feet tall, grow in thickets along streams and on the borders of swamps. The stems have ribs that run from top to bottom. Because the scouring rushes contain a gritty material, they were used by pioneer families as scrub brushes in the days before steel wool. Their giant ancestors grew in many parts of the world during that swampy era several hundred million years ago.

The giant club mosses and horsetails have been of great benefit to mankind. When each tree died, it toppled into the swamp, where the action of warmth and water turned it into muck. As the world's climate changed, the swamps dried and the muck became a substance we call peat, which is used for fuel in some regions. Where conditions were right, pressure from above turned the peat into bituminous, or "soft," coal, and then into anthracite, or "hard," coal. Our modern industrial age has been powered in great measure by these fossil horsetail and club moss forests of long ago.

Scouring Rushes *Horsetails—sterile and fertile stems*

Living fossils that everyone knows are the ferns, those attractive leafy plants found in the cool forests of the north and the steaming jungles of the tropics. Ferns stand midway in the evolutionary scale of plants. They are more advanced than the mosses and mushrooms, because they have roots and stems that let them draw nourishment from the soil, and leaves that take energy from the sunlight. But they reproduce by spores, not by flowers and seeds, and that is what sets them apart from the highest group of plants.

About six thousand species of ferns are known today. They are found on every continent but Antarctica, and in almost every sort of climate. Most of them are small, and in the United States few ferns are more than five or six feet tall. In the tropical countries, tree ferns are found. They grow thirty to fifty feet high, with thick woody trunks.

These tree ferns are directly descended from the giant ferns of the ancient forests. At a time when none of our modern trees had evolved, ferns more than two hundred feet high towered over the swamps. Some of these had leaves twelve feet long. The ferns first appeared in the Devonian, and grew steadily larger through the Mississippian and Pennsylvanian Periods that followed. Those two periods are the only major geological time divisions that are named for American regions. All the others take their names from places in Europe, where the rocks of each period were first identified—Devonian from Devon, in England; Cambrian from the Latin name of Wales; Permian from Perm, in Russia; and so on.

European scientists prefer to class the Mississippian and Pennsylvanian together as the *Carboniferous* ("coal-bearing") Period. The rocks of the Mississippian and Pennsylvanian are indeed coal-bearing, since those were the periods when the giant forests existed. Many huge tree ferns joined the club mosses and horsetails to create the coal deposits that are so important to us today.

None of the modern tree ferns are exactly like their Carboniferous ancestors, but the relationship is close enough so they can be called living fossils. Tree ferns live only where the weather is hot and the rainfall is heavy. They are most common in Australia, New Zealand, and South America. In the United States, the best place to see them is Hawaii. They are also found in the rain forests of Puerto Rico and other Caribbean islands.

The tree ferns have spongy-looking brown trunks, often covered with roots that sprout in mid-air, and strips of stem fiber that give the fern a shaggy appearance. The stalks of fallen leaves mark the upper portion of the trunk, and at the very top is a crown of feathery leaves, ten to fifteen feet in length. One kind of tree fern from Norfolk Island, in the Pacific, reaches heights of eighty feet.

Another tree fern found in Java is covered with curly golden-brown "hair." Rumors of this fern reached Europe in medieval times and gave rise to an amusing botanical fantasy. The scholars who examined samples

Tree Ferns

of the "hair" sent from Java concocted tales of a wonderful creature that was part lamb, part plant. It grew on a stalk a yard high, they said, but grazed on vegetation. When all the plants within reach were eaten, the animal died. Not until 1725 did a botanist expose this Asiatic "lamb" as simply a fuzzy fern!

Ferns, as we have noted, are spore-producers. But during the Mississippian a special type of fern evolved that stood a step closer to the flowering plants. This was the group of seed-bearing ferns, which led the way to the next stage of plant evolution. They are all extinct today.

The seed ferns were unknown until late in the nineteenth century. A flood near Gilboa, New York, cut through the ground and laid bare a whole grove of fossil seed ferns, some of them originally thirty feet high with trunks three feet thick. Instead of spores, they carried true seeds. They were not recognized as seed ferns immediately, because no one expected to find seeds on a fern, fossil or otherwise. Not until 1920, when the building of a dam in the same area unearthed more fossil specimens, were the seeds noticed. The seed ferns are now understood to be a no-longer-missing link between ferns and flowering plants. About fifty different species are known, ranging from Devonian times to the Mesozoic. They apparently died out during the era of the dinosaurs.

Several relatives of the seed ferns remain. They are classed in the highest phylum, the *Spermatophyta*, or seed-bearers. However, they are placed at the bottom of that phylum, since they are the most primitive seed-bearing plants. They are grouped with the gymnosperms, or "naked-seeded plants."

Gymnosperms get their name because their seeds have little protection. They may be enclosed in a cone while developing, but when the cone opens the little seeds have no other covering. All the evergreen trees belong to the gymnosperms, as well as the living fossils we are about to discuss. The highest group of plants are the angiosperms, or "covered-seeded plants." Some angiosperms protect their seeds with a solid jacket—the acorn is a good example. Others wrap them in a fruit, and so we get apples, tomatoes, and berries.

Although they are considered more primitive than the covered-seeded plants, most of the naked-seeded ones are too recent to class as living fossils. A few, however, definitely qualify.

The cycads, which are the nearest living relatives of the seed ferns, are certainly ancient. They saw the dinosaurs come and go, and saw the forests of the covered-seeded plants spread throughout the world. They are still here, though only the botanists seem to know it. Many people have seen cycads without realizing it, thinking that they were some sort of palm trees.

Palms, though, are covered-seeded plants, as anyone who has ever seen a coconut or a date will realize. They are not particularly old as a plant group, and they are not related to the cycads. Yet everyone—even the botanists—lumps palms and cycads together. The scientific name of the cycads, *Cycas,* comes from the Greek word *kykas,* "palm tree." And the best-known cycads are known popularly as palms. The sago palm, the nut palm, the fern palm—all of them are cycads.

Cycads are plants with short, thick trunks never more than a few feet high. At the top of the stocky trunk is

Cycad

a cluster of stiff, dark-green leaves. At the crest of the cycad is a cone that contains the reproductive organs. One organ produces pollen, the other the ova or eggs that the pollen must fertilize.

Eighty-seven species of cycad are living today. Only four are found in the United States. These are all forms of the sago palm, which grows in dry, hot places in Florida. The other cycads come from tropical countries, though a few have been brought to Florida and California as ornamental plants. Many of the "palm frond" decorations at church services are really cycad fronds, for the leaves of the cycad are stiffer and glossier than palm leaves, and keep longer.

In the Mesozoic, cycads were much more widespread. At one time two fifths of all the plant forms in the world were cycads. If that were true today, we would have more than forty thousand different kinds. Fossil cycads have been found in Europe, Greenland, Alaska, Oregon, Australia, and Antarctica. That does not mean that the ancient cycads were sturdy enough to withstand the bitter cold of the North and South Poles. Rather, we think, the Arctic and the Antarctic were much warmer in the Mesozoic than they are now. Most of the cycads became extinct at the end of the Mesozoic.

Cycads are extremely long-lived plants, not only as a family but as individuals. The age of a cycad can be discovered by counting the scars where old leaf clusters once were attached to the trunk. Cycad trunks are covered with a kind of armor made up of these leaf scars.

Every cycad shows several crowns of leaves. At the top is the newest leaf cluster. Below it is last year's crown, sticking out at an angle, and below that is a drooping bunch of even older leaves. The oldest leaves eventually break off. An inch or so of the stem remains to mark the place where each leaf was attached to the trunk. Botanists can tell the age of a cycad by counting the number of such scars on the trunk.

Some cycads grow a new crown twice a year, others once a year or every other year. An expert on cycads—and there are not many of them—has to know how often the leaves sprout before he can decide how old a cycad is. Professor Charles J. Chamberlain of the University of Chicago published a book in 1919 called *The Living Cycads,* telling of his attempts to measure cycad ages. He worked with a Mexican cycad species that forms a new crown every other year. Each crown has about twenty leaves, so this cycad produces an average of ten new leaves a year. When he counted the leaf scars on a specimen with a trunk about six feet tall, they numbered ten thousand. So this one rather short cycad was a thousand years old!

Professor Chamberlain thought that many cycads could live well over a thousand years. Certain pine trees live for four thousand years, and the giant redwoods of California are nearly as long-lived. Even so, it was surprising to find these palmlike survivors of the dinosaur era attaining such great ages.

Cycads have a number of uses for man. They make

decorative garden plants where the climate is mild enough for them. The root of the sago palm can be chopped and grated to make a starchy pudding. The Indians of Florida and Central America made such cycad puddings, but when soldiers used sago palms for food during the Civil War a number of them died. What the soldiers did not know, and the Indians did, was that the roots contain a poison that has to be washed out before they can be used for food. (It always seems puzzling how such things are discovered. Who was the first Indian brave enough to try it?)

Cycad leaves, as mentioned, are used for decorations. The seeds of some cycads are ground up to make flour for bread, both in Mexico and in South Africa. In the East Indies, young cycad leaves are cooked as vegetables. Animals find cycad seeds and leaves good to eat also. Despite all this, cycads have flourished for more than 150 million years.

One small group of gymnosperms stands alone—the aardvarks of the plant world, perhaps. They are the *Ginkgoales*, an order that has just one member, the ginkgo tree. The ginkgo cannot claim any plant on earth as a close relative.

In the days of the dinosaurs, ginkgo trees lived everywhere in the world. Africa is the only continent that has not yielded fossil ginkgos, perhaps because the scientists have not been looking in the proper places. Ancient ginkgos have been found in Alaska and Australia, Sweden and Patagonia, England and Mongolia, Italy and the United States. The ginkgos of 150 million years ago do not look very different from those of today. At the close of the Mesozoic, ginkgos vanished from most parts of the world, but survived in China and Japan.

The ginkgo is an unusual-looking tree, though you have to look carefully to see how it is different from the everyday maples and oaks and birches. The branches of our familiar trees fork outward and upward, but a ginkgo's boughs stick out almost at right angles. The tree usually will have a few branches longer than all the others, giving it an oddly lopsided look. Also, the well-known trees have small branches sprouting from the big ones, and twigs growing from the small branches. The ginkgo lacks these medium-sized boughs, and the twigs sprout right from the main limbs.

The ginkgo's leaves are small and fan-shaped. They look like the leaves of the maidenhair fern. For that reason the ginkgo is sometimes called the "maidenhair tree." Each leaf is divided into two segments or lobes, which explains the tree's scientific name of *Ginkgo biloba.* The ginkgo seedling's first leaves are four-lobed, like those of some fossil species from the Mesozoic. But the two-lobed leaves appear as the seedling gets older.

The ginkgo leaf has unusual veins, too. If you look at a leaf of a common forest tree, you will see that there is one chief vein running down the center, with smaller veins branching from it like limbs branching from a tree trunk. The ginkgo leaf has no central vein. All its veins spread out from the stem, like the ribs of a fan.

Though the ginkgo is classed with the naked-seeded plants because of its many primitive features, its seed actually is covered with fleshy fruit. Ginkgo fruits hang in clusters, like little wrinkled apricots or cherries, and are so numerous that the fallen ones form a kind of carpet around the tree. The ginkgo fruit has little taste when fresh. It takes on an unpleasant smell as it decays. Within the fruit is a "nut" like a cherry pit. These are roasted and eaten in China and Japan. Despite the fleshy wrapper, the ginkgo still belongs with the gymnosperms. It is the exception to the general rule about the seeds of gymnosperms, but resembles them in other ways.

The Orient has long admired the ginkgo tree. It survived in remote forest groves of Asia after it disappeared from the rest of the world, and the Chinese, who called it the "duck's foot tree," from the shape of its leaves, planted it in their cities. The Japanese did the same. Large ginkgos, a hundred feet tall and more, are found near many Chinese and Japanese temples. One, in northern Japan, has been worshiped for more than a thousand years. Japanese peasants think that the ginkgo is a protection against fire. It is thought to have this magical quality because it is extremely tough, and comes unharmed through fires that destroy neighboring trees. The ginkgo is also able to resist the effects of very cold weather, of insect pests, and of fungus infections. In the twentieth century it has shown itself rugged

Ginkgo

enough to withstand the smoke and gasoline fumes of big cities. Short of chopping it down, it is very difficult to kill a ginkgo tree.

The first European to see ginkgos was a German physician, naturalist, and world traveler, Dr. Engelbrecht Kaempfer. In 1681, at the age of thirty, Kaempfer was studying medicine and science in Sweden when that country's king sent an embassy to Persia. Kaempfer took a job as secretary to the ambassador. When the Swedish party headed home from Persia in 1684, Kaempfer decided to see more of the Far East, and signed on with the Dutch East India Company. The year 1690 saw him as physician to the Dutch ambassador in Nagasaki, Japan. As soon as he arrived, he discovered the magnificent groves of ginkgos growing near the temples of Nagasaki. (Neither the ginkgos nor the temples are there any more. In 1945 the United States dropped an atomic bomb on Nagasaki, bringing the Second World War to a dramatic end.)

In 1712, after his return to Europe, Kaempfer published a book that included a description of the ginkgo. *Ginkgo* was the Chinese name for the tree, he said, and the Japanese called it *itsio*. He knew that *gin*, in Chinese, meant "silver," and he thought that ginkgo might mean "silver apricot," describing the fruit of the tree. As it happens, there is no such word in Chinese. What Kaempfer may have heard was *sankyo*, meaning "hill apricot." But *ginkgo* was the name he gave, and the name has stuck.

His book aroused some interest in the unusual Chinese tree. Before long, the ginkgo, which had once lived everywhere and then had dwindled to a few places in Asia, began to reconquer the world. A ginkgo tree was planted in Holland about 1730, at the botanical garden of the University of Utrecht. An old ginkgo tree still grows there, and may very well be the original one. About twenty years later, ginkgo seeds from Japan reached England, and by 1768 a ginkgo was recorded in Austria. They remained rare trees, owned only by the wealthy. One problem was that ginkgos are either male or female, and unless both kinds of ginkgos stand side by side no seeds will be produced. That made the spread of ginkgos in Europe slow.

Slow but sure, however. The price of ginkgos fell as the trees multiplied. In 1784, a rich Philadelphian introduced the ginkgo to the United States, planting some on his estate. The trees flourished. When Thomas Jefferson was President, in 1806, he received a ginkgo from the Philadelphia grower as a gift for his garden. By the middle of the nineteenth century, ginkgos were common on city streets. Because they are so sturdy, ginkgos are popular in such automobile-choked cities as New York and Washington, D.C., where gasoline fumes kill weaker trees. Some streets are lined with ginkgos for block after block.

The ginkgo spread so rapidly because it was a rare, interesting tree from Asia, and people were curious about it. They might have been much more fascinated if they had known it was also a living fossil. The first fossil ginkgos were discovered in Italy about 1850. They looked just like modern ginkgos, but they were preserved in rocks 50 million years old.

Those were still pretty recent specimens, as ginkgos go. Early in the twentieth century, ginkgos of the dinosaur era—the Mesozoic—were found. They were common in rocks of all three periods of the Mesozoic, the Cretaceous, the Jurassic, and the Triassic. Triassic ginkgos, 170 million years old, were slightly different from modern ones, but not so much that they could easily be told apart.

The ginkgo story does not seem to begin there. Fossils from the Permian Period, older even than the dinosaurs, have a ginkgolike look. Even back in the Pennsylvanian, when the coal forests grew, certain trees appear to be ginkgo ancestors. It is possible that the ginkgo is one of the most ancient of all living fossils.

If that is so, and if the ginkgo is so sturdy, why did it become extinct in most parts of the world? There is no easy answer. Today the ginkgo does well under conditions that the newer kinds of trees find too much to take. Yet millions of years ago these newcomers of the forest were able to push the ginkgo aside. We may never know why.

Today the ginkgo is established all over the world once more—ready for another few hundred million years of life. Though it is found on the streets of every city, the sight of it still can set the spine tingling. As

Sir Algernon Seward, an English botanist who wrote on ancient plant life, declared, the ginkgo is "much more to us than a mere tree . . . it gives us glimpses of the great procession of life and the building of the world in which we live."

The last of our living fossils belongs to an order of gymnosperms called *Gnetales.* These are shrubs with naked seeds, but having flowers and internal structure that seem linked to the covered-seed plants. They appear to hold a place somewhere between the gymnosperms and the angiosperms.

Most of the plants of this group evolved quite recently, so far as we know. One, however, has scarcely changed at all since the Permian Period. It is as ancient as the tuatara—older than the dinosaurs by millions of years. Few plants are stranger than this one, which bears the scientific name of *Welwitschia mirabilis.*

The name means "the wonderful plant of Welwitch," and *wonderful* is the right word. It is named for its discoverer, Friedrich Welwitsch, a German explorer who found it in the desert of Southwest Africa in 1860. It grows nowhere else.

Welwitschia would look like a giant radish or carrot if pulled from the ground. It consists of a woody trunk three or four feet thick. Only a foot or so sticks out above the ground, and the rest goes deep into the soil, five to ten feet down.

In its hundred-odd years of life, a *Welwitschia* grows

only two leaves. There are no branches or twigs, and the leaves sprout right from the top of the trunk. They are tough, leathery straps, which spread out over the ground like ribbons. The leaves are two to four feet wide and up to twelve feet long. They keep on growing all through the plant's long life. Veins run the length of these curious leaves, but there are no crosswise veins that might give added strength to them. As a result, *Welwitschia's* leaves fray at the tip, and rip lengthwise in high winds. This produces a shredding effect, so that the leaves become ragged streamers, torn and tattered into many narrower ribbons.

There it lies, baking under the African sun, whipped about by the desert storms, its two threadbare leaves sprawling three or four yards over the hot sand. It looks like something planted by a visitor from Mars. *Welwitschia* is the product of our own world, though—the world of 200 million years ago. Evolution gave it its unique form, and then left it alone, and there it remains, forgotten by time.

Welwitschia

Twelve:

LIVING FOSSILS TO COME

ABOUT A HUNDRED FIFTY YEARS ago, Georges Cuvier was ready to declare zoology a closed science. All the large animals of the world had been discovered, Cuvier said. There was no need to search any longer. But the okapi, the Asian tapir, and many other discoveries prove how wrong he was.

Another man, in the 1840's wanted to close down the United States Patent Office, which he headed. Everything possible had already been invented, he said, so why keep the Patent Office in business? We have the telephone, the airplane, and the electric toothbrush, among other inventions, to show that he was mistaken.

Today there are those who think that the whole world has been explored, and that nature has no secrets left. They, too, are wrong—on both counts. Much of the world is still waiting for exploration. The jungles of New Guinea, the wastelands of central Australia, the trackless reaches of the Amazon Valley, still hold many mysteries. The deep sea has hardly been touched. The age of Antarctic exploration is just beginning. Every day, somewhere in the world, a scientist discovers a plant or an animal that was unknown the day before.

Can we hope that other living fossils will be found in the years to come?

Of course. Most living fossils have survived because they have a talent for keeping out of sight. Most have been discovered only by luck, or after long, intense searching. It is unwise to think we have found them all.

The coelacanth turned up as recently as 1938, after all. *Neopilina* came to light in 1952. We have known the okapi only since 1900, the lungfish of Australia since 1869. Tomorrow morning's newspaper may bring word of other newly discovered living fossils.

If that is the case, what can we expect to find?

Dinosaurs, perhaps? That thought has long been an exciting one—that in some jungle of South America or Africa, a few giant reptiles still linger after their time. Dinosaurs are not likely to be good at hiding themselves, though. It seems reasonable to think that if any of the monstrous beasts had survived, we would have found them by now.

Not all dinosaurs lived on land, however. Some were water creatures that looked like toothy, scaly whales. We think these oceangoing reptiles died out some 70 million years ago, but we used to think that about the coelacanths, too. Does an ancient monster lurk in the oceans? We can't say no—not certainly.

Some reptiles took to the air—those flying dragons, the *pterodactyls*. Again and again, explorers in Africa have told of seeing pterodactyls, though the usual explanation is that they had glimpsed big bats. (Bats and pterodactyls are similar in just one way, their wings, bare and rubbery-looking. But bats are mammals, warm-blooded and hairy.) One such report came from Ivan T. Sanderson, who led an expedition to Africa in 1932. Sanderson was wading in a stream at twilight when a companion suddenly shouted, "Look out!" Then, he writes:

"I let out a shout also and instantly bobbed down under the water, because, coming straight at me only a few feet above the water was a black thing the size of an eagle. I had only a glimpse of its face, yet that was quite sufficient, for its lower jaw hung open and bore a semicircle of pointed white teeth set about their own width apart from each other. . . . Just before it became too dark to see, it came again, hurtling back down the river, its teeth chattering, the air 'shss-shssing' as it was cleft by the great, black, dracula-like wings."

Sanderson thinks he saw a giant bat. At least one reputable zoologist, studying all the details, thinks it might have been a pterodactyl. But if pterodactyls still live in the African jungle, we are still waiting for the first one to be caught.

Scientists in Australia have been puzzled for a long time by reports of another supposedly extinct animal, *Diprotodon*, in the western desert of that continent. *Diprotodon* was a giant wombat as big as a rhinoceros, which is thought to have died out about ten thousand years ago. In 1847, a well-preserved *Diprotodon* was found in an Australian salt lake. It did not look ten thousand years old at all. A famous explorer, Ludwig Leichardt, set out into the Australian desert to look for a live *Diprotodon*, but he vanished on the quest and was never seen again. Since Leichardt's time, many other *Diprotodon* remains have been found, though no living ones. Until that vast desert is completely explored, the possibility still remains that the big beasts survive in it. There are other marsupial mysteries too, such as the "tiger" or "leopard" that has been seen many times over the last hundred years in various parts of Australia. Zoologists have yet to find one, dead or alive.

New Zealand, that other storehouse of odd beasts, has at least one animal in the now-you-see-it-now-you-don't class. It is called *waitoreke* by the natives, and if it really exists it will be a hard one for the scientists to explain.

There are no known native mammals on New Zealand. That country was cut off from its nearest neighbor, Australia, before any mammals evolved. The highest forms of life in New Zealand—before mankind brought some in from outside—were those wingless birds, the kiwis, and their giant relatives, the now-extinct moas.

Yet the natives have long spoken of an otterlike animal living in the rivers and lakes of South Island. Possibly, if it really exists, this animal came with the Maoris when they arrived a thousand years ago. Maybe it is some sort of platypus that managed the sea journey from Australia, or even a true otter that migrated all the way across the Pacific from Japan or even California. There is also the possibility that the waitoreke is an extremely primitive mammal that evolved in New Zealand before the islands were cut off from Australia. It may simply be a myth. Right now, no one knows.

The dream of finding extinct animals alive is a common one. Many scientists have spent time and energy looking for giant ground sloths in South America, for dinosaurs and pterodactyls in Africa, for moas in New Zealand. They have had no luck. On the other hand, Miss Courtenay-Latimer, who was not looking for living fossils at all, had a coelacanth pop out of the sea right at her doorstep. One never knows what surprises are in store. If coelacanths and tuataras can survive, other creatures equally strange, equally ancient, may be with us also. In natural history as in most other fields, the only thing that is certain is that nothing is certain.

FOR FURTHER READING

The following books are general works on natural history which deal with so many of our living fossils that it is simpler to list them here than to include them in the chapter-by-chapter bibliography below. All are well illustrated and entertaining to read, and cover a wide range of subjects:

Burton, Maurice: *Living Fossils.* (Thames & Hudson, London, 1954.) A survey of the entire subject, for college-level readers and up.

Carrington, Richard: *Mermaids and Mastodons.* (Chatto & Windus, London, 1957.) Sections on *Peripatus*, marsupials, ginkgo trees, the coelacanth, etc.

Heuvelmans, Bernard: *On the Track of Unknown Animals.* (Hill and Wang, New York, 1959.) Many animals.

Ley, Willy: *Exotic Zoology.* (Viking Press, New York, 1959.) Amusing and broad coverage of the Animal Kingdom.

Wendt, Herbert: *Out of Noah's Ark.* (Weidenfeld and Nicolson, London, 1959.) Particularly valuable for its many quaint and rare old illustrations.

For other material, see the chapter lists below.

CHAPTER ONE: THE IDEA OF CHANGE

The books in this section are useful for the background information they provide on the evolution theory and on the development of animal and plant life in general, though they do not deal in detail with any of the living fossils:

Brodrick, Alan Houghton: *Man and His Ancestry.* (Hutchinson, London, 1960.) Human evolution.

Colbert, Edwin H.: *Millions of Years Ago.* (Crowell, New York, 1958.) A description for younger readers of many extinct animals. Well illustrated.

Darwin, Charles: *Origin of Species.* There are many reprint editions of this classic work.

Moore, Raymond Cecil: *Introduction to Historical Geology.* (McGraw-Hill, New York, 1949.) Advanced textbook of geology, showing the development of the earth and its inhabitants from the beginning.

Scheele, William E.: *The First Mammals.* (World Publishing Company, Cleveland and New York, 1955.) Superb illustrations, brief text for young readers, about the origin of mammals.

Silverberg, Robert: *Man Before Adam.* (Macrae Smith, Philadelphia, 1964.) Human evolution, with considerable material on the theories of Darwin and on the concepts of animal evolution. For high-school-age readers and up.

CHAPTER TWO: OUT OF THE SEA

Batten, Roger L.: "The Need to Classify." *Natural History,* March 1958. On *Neopilina.*

Buchsbaum, Ralph: *Animals Without Backbones.* (Revised edition, University of Chicago, 1948.) On *Neopilina,* horseshoe crab, cephalopods, crinoids, etc. A basic work.

Cowen, Robert C.: *Frontiers of the Sea.* (Doubleday, New York, 1960. Paperback edition, Bantam Pathfinder Books, New York, 1963.) Covers the field of oceanographic research, with sections on the seagoing living fossils.

Idyll, C. P.: *Abyss—The Deep Sea and the Creatures That Live In It.* (Crowell, New York, 1964.) Covers much of the same material as the Cowen book above, but with more emphasis on natural history, and a more detailed treatment. Excellent illustrations.

Lane, Frank W.: *Kingdom of the Octopus.* (Sheridan House, New York, 1960. Paperback edition, Pyramid Books, New York, 1962.) An excellent account of all the cephalopods, living fossils and otherwise.

Yonge, C. M.: "The Galathea Deep Sea Expedition." *New Biology,* Number 25, January 1958. The discovery of *Neopilina.*

CHAPTER THREE: THE JOINTED-LEGGED ONES

Sections in Burton, Carrington, and Buchsbaum as listed above.

CHAPTER FOUR: THE FINNY FOSSILS

Bracker, Milton: "Coelacanth Saga." *The New York Times Magazine*, October 6, 1963.

McCormick, Harold W., and Tom Allen, with Captain William E. Young: *Shadows in the Sea.* (Chilton Books, Philadelphia, 1963.) The most recent and best of the books about sharks, with a complete account of each type, and many fine illustrations.

Millot, Jacques: "The Coelacanth." *Scientific American*, December 1955.

CHAPTER FIVE: THE THREE-EYED ONE, AND OTHERS

For tuatara, see Burton, Ley, and Wendt as listed above.

Ley, Willy: *Salamanders and Other Wonders.* (Viking Press, New York, 1955.) Among much else, the book contains a lively chapter on the Galapagos tortoises.

CHAPTER SIX: BIRDS THAT DON'T FLY

Chapman, Walker: *The Loneliest Continent.* (New York Graphic Society, Greenwich, Conn., 1964.) History of Antarctic exploration.

Cutright, Paul Russell: *The Great Naturalists Explore South America.* (Macmillan, New York, 1940.) Chapter on the rhea, and one on the hoatzin.

Dixon, Charles: *Lost and Vanishing Birds.* (John Macqueen, London, 1898.) Chapter on the kiwi.

Murphy, Robert Cushman: "History of the Penguins." *Natural History*, March 1959.

Sladen, William J. L.: "Penguins." *Scientific American*, December 1957.

CHAPTER SEVEN: WOMBATS, WALLABIES, AND BANDICOOTS

Fleay, David: "Strange Animals of the Island Continent." *National Geographic Magazine*, September 1963.

Reynolds, Harold C.: "The Opossum." *Scientific American*, June 1953. Natural history of the American opossum.

CHAPTER EIGHT: MAMMALS THAT LAY EGGS

Fleay, David: "Flight of the Platypuses." *National Geographic Magazine*, October 1958.

CHAPTER NINE: SOME PUZZLING ANTEATERS

See Cutright, *Great Naturalists Explore South America*, and Ley, *Exotic Zoology*.

CHAPTER TEN: FOSSILS OF THE FOREST

See Cutright and the books listed in the general reference section.

CHAPTER ELEVEN: LIVING FOSSILS OF THE PLANT KINGDOM

Hylander, Clarence J.: *The World of Plant Life*. (Macmillan, New York, 1944.)

Ley, Willy: *Dragons in Amber*. (Viking Press, New York, 1951.) Chapters on ginkgos and cycads.

Index

ABOUT THE AUTHOR

Robert Silverberg was born and grew up in New York City, where he makes his home today. He was graduated from Columbia University, and even before he was out of college, a number of his short stories had been published. He is the author of numerous fiction and nonfiction books.

Mr. Silverberg collects rare books on the subjects which especially interest him: archaeology, history, science, and exploration. He has traveled in various parts of the United States, Europe, and the West Indies.

ABOUT THE ILLUSTRATOR

Leonard Everett Fisher received both a B.F.A. and an M.F.A. from the Yale University School of Fine Arts. During World War II he interrupted his studies to serve in the Army as a topographic editor and a photogrammetrist (making maps from photographs).

Mr. Fisher, who has illustrated more than one hundred books and is the author of nine, has served as dean of the Whitney School of Art in New Haven, Connecticut. His work has been represented in many of the nation's top exhibitions.